GRADE

2

Curriculum Units

How Many Floors? How Many Rooms?

Patterns, Functions, and Change

UNIT 5

Complicated Kris Northern

"This image illustrates some of the best qualities of fractals—infinity, reiteration, and self similarity."– **Kris Northern**

Investigations
IN NUMBER, DATA, AND SPACE®

Glenview, Illinois • Boston, Massachusetts
Chandler, Arizona • Upper Saddle River, New Jersey

The Investigations curriculum was developed by TERC, Cambridge, MA.

This material is based on work supported by the National Science Foundation ("NSF") under Grant No. ESI-0095450. Any opinions, findings, and conclusions or recommendations expressed in this material are those of the author(s) and do not necessarily reflect the views of the National Science Foundation.

ISBN-13: 978-0-328-60015-1

ISBN-10: 0-328-60015-6

2 3 4 5 6 7 8 9 10 V003 14 13 12 11

T E R C

Co-Principal Investigators

Susan Jo Russell

Karen Economopoulos

Authors

Lucy Wittenberg
Director Grades 3–5

Karen Economopoulos
Director Grades K–2

Virginia Bastable
(SummerMath for Teachers,
Mt. Holyoke College)

Katie Hickey Bloomfield

Keith Cochran

Darrell Earnest

Arusha Hollister

Nancy Horowitz

Erin Leidl

Megan Murray

Young Oh

Beth W. Perry

Susan Jo Russell

Deborah Schifter
(Education
Development Center)

Kathy Sillman

Note: Unless otherwise noted, all contributors listed above were staff of the Education Research Collaborative at TERC during their work on the curriculum. Other affiliations during the time of development are listed.

Administrative Staff

Amy Taber
Project Manager

Beth Bergeron

Lorraine Brooks

Emi Fujiwara

Contributing Authors

Denise Baumann

Jennifer DiBrienza

Hollee Freeman

Paula Hooper

Jan Mokros

Stephen Monk
(University of Washington)

Mary Beth O'Connor

Judy Storeygard

Cornelia Tierney

Elizabeth Van Cleef

Carol Wright

Technology

Jim Hammerman

Classroom Field Work

Amy Appell

Rachel E. Davis

Traci Higgins

Julia Thompson

Collaborating Teachers

This group of dedicated teachers carried out extensive field testing in their classrooms, met regularly to discuss issues of teaching and learning mathematics, provided feedback to staff, welcomed staff into their classrooms to document students' work, and contributed both suggestions and written material that has been incorporated into the curriculum.

Bethany Altchek

Linda Amaral

Kimberly Beauregard

Barbara Bernard

Nancy Buell

Rose Christiansen

Chris Colbath-Hess

Lisette Colon

Kim Cook

Frances Cooper

Kathleen Drew

Rebeka Eston Salemi

Thomas Fisher

Michael Flynn

Holly Ghazey

Susan Gillis

Danielle Harrington

Elaine Herzog

Francine Hiller

Kirsten Lee Howard

Liliana Klass

Leslie Kramer

Melissa Lee Andrichak

Kelley Lee Sadowski

Jennifer Levitan

Mary Lou LoVecchio

Kristen McEnaney

Maura McGrail

Kathe Millett

Florence Molyneaux

Amy Monkiewicz

Elizabeth Monopoli

Carol Murray

Robyn Musser

Christine Norrman

Deborah O'Brien

Timothy O'Connor

Anne Marie O'Reilly

Mark Paige

Margaret Riddle

Karen Schweitzer

Elisabeth Seyferth

Susan Smith

Debra Sorvillo

Shoshanah Starr

Janice Szymaszek

Karen Tobin

JoAnn Trauschke

Ana Vaisenstein

Yvonne Watson

Michelle Woods

Mary Wright

Advisors

Deborah Lowenberg Ball,
University of Michigan

Hyman Bass, Professor of Mathematics and Mathematics Education
University of Michigan

Mary Canner, Principal, Natick Public Schools

Thomas Carpenter, Professor of Curriculum and Instruction,
University of Wisconsin-Madison

Janis Freckmann, Elementary Mathematics Coordinator,
Milwaukee Public Schools

Lynne Godfrey, Mathematics Coach,
Cambridge Public Schools

Ginger Hanlon, Instructional Specialist in Mathematics,
New York City Public Schools

DeAnn Huinker, Director, Center for Mathematics and
Science Education Research, University of Wisconsin-Milwaukee

James Kaput, Professor of Mathematics, University of
Massachusetts-Dartmouth

Kate Kline, Associate Professor, Department of Mathematics
and Statistics, Western Michigan University

Jim Lewis, Professor of Mathematics,
University of Nebraska-Lincoln

William McCallum, Professor of Mathematics,
University of Arizona

Harriet Pollatsek, Professor of Mathematics,
Mount Holyoke College

Debra Shein-Gerson, Elementary Mathematics Specialist,
Weston Public Schools

Gary Shevell, Assistant Principal,
New York City Public Schools

Liz Sweeney, Elementary Math Department,
Boston Public Schools

Lucy West, Consultant, Metamorphosis:
Teaching Learning Communities, Inc.

This revision of the curriculum was built on the work of the many authors who contributed to the first edition (published between 1994 and 1998). We acknowledge the critical contributions of these authors in developing the content and pedagogy of *Investigations*:

Authors

Joan Akers

Michael T. Battista

Douglas H. Clements

Karen Economopoulos

Marlene Kliman

Jan Mokros

Megan Murray

Ricardo Nemirovsky

Andee Rubin

Susan Jo Russell

Cornelia Tierney

Contributing Authors

Mary Berle-Carman

Rebecca B. Corwin

Rebeka Eston

Claryce Evans

Anne Goodrow

Cliff Konold

Chris Mainhart

Sue McMillen

Jerrie Moffet

Tracy Noble

Kim O'Neil

Mark Ogonowski

Julie Sarama

Amy Shulman Weinberg

Margie Singer

Virginia Woolley

Tracey Wright

UNIT 5

How Many Floors? How Many Rooms?

Investigations

Overview of Program Components

FOR TEACHERS

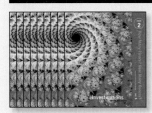

The **Curriculum Units** are the teaching guides. (See far right.)

Implementing Investigations in Grade 2 offers suggestions for implementing the curriculum. It also contains a comprehensive index.

The **Differentiation and Intervention Guide** offers additional activities for each Investigation to support the range of learners.

Investigations for the Interactive Whiteboard provides whole-class instructional support to enhance each session.

The **Resource Masters and Transparencies CD** contains all reproducible materials that support instruction. The **Shapes CD** provides an environment in which students investigate a variety of geometric ideas.

FOR STUDENTS

The **Student Activity Book** contains the consumable student pages (Recording Sheets, Homework, Practice, and so on).

The **Student Math Handbook** contains Math Words and Ideas pages and Games directions.

The *Investigations* Curriculum

Investigations in Number, Data, and Space® is a K–5 mathematics curriculum designed to engage students in making sense of mathematical ideas. Six major goals guided the development of the *Investigations in Number, Data, and Space*® curriculum. The curriculum is designed to:

- Support students to make sense of mathematics and learn that they can be mathematical thinkers

- Focus on computational fluency with whole numbers as a major goal of the elementary grades

- Provide substantive work in important areas of mathematics—rational numbers, geometry, measurement, data, and early algebra—and connections among them

- Emphasize reasoning about mathematical ideas

- Communicate mathematics content and pedagogy to teachers

- Engage the range of learners in understanding mathematics

Underlying these goals are three guiding principles that are touchstones for the *Investigations* team as we approach both students and teachers as agents of their own learning:

1. *Students have mathematical ideas.* Students come to school with ideas about numbers, shapes, measurements, patterns, and data. If given the opportunity to learn in an environment that stresses making sense of mathematics, students build on the ideas they already have and learn about new mathematics they have never encountered. Students learn that they are capable of having mathematical ideas, applying what they know to new situations, and thinking and reasoning about unfamiliar problems.

2. *Teachers are engaged in ongoing learning* about mathematics content, pedagogy, and student learning. The curriculum provides material for professional development, to be used by teachers individually or in groups, that supports teachers' continued learning as they use the curriculum over several years. The *Investigations* curriculum materials are designed as much to be a dialogue with teachers as to be a core of content for students.

3. *Teachers collaborate with the students and curriculum materials* to create the curriculum as enacted in the classroom. The only way for a good curriculum to be used well is for teachers to be active participants in implementing it. Teachers use the curriculum to maintain a clear, focused, and coherent agenda for mathematics teaching. At the same time, they observe and listen carefully to students, try to understand how they are thinking, and make teaching decisions based on these observations.

Investigations is based on experience from research and practice, including field testing that involved documentation of thousands of hours in classrooms, observations of students, input from teachers, and analysis of student work. As a result, the curriculum addresses the learning needs of real students in a wide range of classrooms and communities. The investigations are carefully designed to invite all students into mathematics—girls and boys; members of diverse cultural, ethnic, and language groups; and students with a wide variety of strengths, needs, and interests.

Based on this extensive classroom testing, the curriculum takes seriously the time students need to develop a strong conceptual foundation and skills based on that foundation. Each curriculum unit focuses on an area of content in depth, providing time for students to develop and practice ideas across a variety of activities and contexts that build on each other. Daily guidelines for time spent on class sessions, Classroom Routines (K–3), and Ten-Minute Math (3–5) reflect the commitment to devoting adequate time to mathematics in each school day.

About This Curriculum Unit

This **Curriculum Unit** is one of nine teaching guides in Grade 2. The fifth unit in Grade 2 is *How Many Floors? How Many Rooms?*

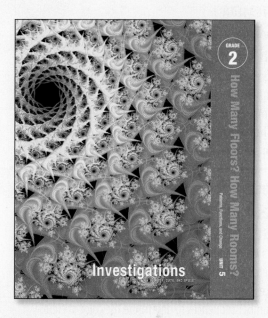

- The **Introduction and Overview** section organizes and presents the instructional materials, provides background information, and highlights important features specific to this unit.

- Each Curriculum Unit contains several **Investigations.** Each Investigation focuses on a set of related mathematical ideas.

- Investigations are divided into one-hour **Sessions,** or lessons.

- Sessions have a combination of these parts: **Activity, Discussion, Math Workshop, Assessment Activity,** and **Session Follow-Up.**

- Each session also has one or more **Classroom Routines** that are done outside of math time.

- At the back of the book is a collection of **Teacher Notes** and **Dialogue Boxes** that provide professional development related to the unit.

- Also included at the back of the book are the **Student Math Handbook** pages for this unit.

- The **Index** provides a way to look up important words or terms.

Overview

O F   T H I S   U N I T

Investigation	Session	Day	
INVESTIGATION 1 **Growing Patterns: Ratio and Equal Groups** Students construct cube buildings that have a constant ratio of "rooms" to "floors," and use tables to represent how the total number of rooms changes in relation to the number of floors. They also use tables to represent ratio relationships between the areas of faces of the pattern block shapes.	**1.1** How Many Floors? How Many Rooms?	1	
	1.2 Using Tables to Record	2	
	1.3 Comparing Tables	3	
	1.4 Assessment: Understanding Tables	4	
	1.5 Ratio Relationships with Pattern Blocks	5	
	1.6 Ratio Relationships with Pattern Blocks, *continued*	6	
INVESTIGATION 2 **Repeating Patterns and Number Sequences** Students make and describe repeating patterns with body movements and colored cubes. They associate number sequences with the colors in their cube patterns, and use these number sequences to determine the color of cubes that are farther along in the sequence.	**2.1** Cube Train Patterns	7	
	2.2 Counting by 2s	8	
	2.3 Counting by 3s	9	
	2.4 How Is Red–Blue–Brown–Green Like Yellow–Black–White–Orange?	10	
	2.5 End-of-Unit Assessment	11	

Each *Investigations* session has some combination of these five parts: **Activity, Discussion, Math Workshop, Assessment Activity,** and **Session Follow-Up.** These session parts are indicated in the chart below. Each session also has one **Classroom Routine** that is done outside of math time.

 **W** Interactive Whiteboard

Activity	Discussion	Math Workshop	Assessment Activity	Session Follow-Up
(W) ●	(W)			●
(W) (W)	(W)			●
● (W)	(W)			●
	(W)	●	●	●
(W) (W)		●	●	●
	●	●	●	●
● (W)	(W)			●
(W)	(W)			●
(W)	(W)			●
●	(W) (W)			●
			(W)	●

Classroom Routines

What Time Is It?	Quick Images	Today's Number	How Many Pockets?
	(W)		
		(W)	
(W)			
			(W)
	(W)		
		(W)	
(W)			
	(W)		
		(W)	
(W)			
	(W)		

Mathematics

How Many Floors? How Many Rooms? is part of the patterns, functions, and change strand of *Investigations*. These units develop ideas about patterns, sequences, and functions and are part of the early algebra foundation integrated into the curriculum.

In the Grade 1 unit, *Color, Shape, and Number Patterns,* students constructed, described, and extended repeating patterns using connecting cubes as well as body movement patterns (such as clap–snap fingers–clap–snap fingers). Students created and described AB, ABC, AAB, ABB, ABCD, and other patterns. They identifed the unit of the pattern (the part of a pattern that repeats) and compared how repeating patterns are the same and different. When students compared a red–yellow–green pattern with a blue–black–white pattern, they noticed that while the colors are different, the ABC structure of the pattern is the same. A clap–slap knees–touch shoulders body movement pattern also has the same ABC unit. This work with repeating patterns is extended in Investigation 2 of this unit. Comparing situations within and between different contexts will also continue in this unit as students explain how two different ratio situations can result in the same table in Investigation 1.

In Grade 1, students also worked with three different growing patterns, patterns in which there is a constant increase: staircase towers made with cubes, the penny jar, and pattern block sequences. In these situations, they encountered number sequences, including the sequence of the multiples of two and the sequence of the multiples of three. Students should be familiar with the idea of "counting by" a number—they counted by groups of two, five, and ten in *Stickers, Number Strings, and Story Problems* this year. In the same unit, they worked with counting by 2s, starting at zero and starting at one, and defined the odd and even numbers. Students need not know all the "counting by" sequences, such as counting by 3s, in order to engage in the work of this unit, but can figure them out by counting or adding. Students have also worked with

ratios in their previous work (e.g., the number of noses, eyes, or fingers for a certain number of people).

This unit focuses on 3 Mathematical Emphases:

1 Linear Relationships **Describing and representing ratios**

Math Focus Points

- ◆ Describing the relationship between two quantities in a constant ratio situation
- ◆ Using tables to represent the ratio relationship between two quantities
- ◆ Finding the value of one quantity in a constant ratio situation, given the value of the other

Second graders are familiar with situations in which they encounter equal groups: two cookies per person, six juice cans in a pack, five fingers on a hand, and so forth. However, they do not necessarily think about how these ratios (2 to 1 or 2:1, 6 to 1 or 6:1, and 5 to 1 or 5:1) can be expressed in many pairs of numbers. For example, if there are six juice cans in a pack, there are 12 juice cans in two packs, 18 juice cans in three packs, and so forth. These pairs of numbers—6:1, 12:2, and 18:3—all express an underlying 6-to-1 relationship, a constant ratio between the two quantities.

In Investigation 1, students explore ratio situations like these in two contexts: cube buildings and pattern blocks. Each cube building has a floor plan, and all of the floors of the building are identical. So a building with three cubes or "rooms" on one floor has a total of six rooms when a second floor is built on, and a total of nine rooms when the third floor is built on. Covering one shape of pattern block with another shape also produces these kinds of patterns. It takes two of the red trapezoids to cover one of the yellow hexagons, four trapezoids to cover two hexagons, six trapezoids to cover three hexagons, and so forth. In both of these contexts, students build models and record how one variable changes in relation to the other. They use what they are learning to determine quantities later in the series. How many rooms will there be in ten floors? How many trapezoids will it take to cover ten hexagons? As students engage in this work, they are continually thinking about equal groups. They solve problems by adding or counting by 2s, 3s, 4s, 5s, and 6s.

Situations that look very different may have the same underlying constant ratio. For example, a building with six rooms per floor and the relationship between triangles and hexagons in the pattern block set have the same 6:1 ratio. A building with two floors has 12 rooms; two hexagons can be covered exactly by 12 triangles. By comparing tables that show these different relationships, both within the same context and between the two contexts (cube buildings and pattern blocks), students notice how different situations can have the same underlying relationship between quantities.

Total Number of Floors	Total Number of Rooms	Total Number of Hexagons	Total Number of Triangles
1	6	1	6
2	12	2	12
3	18	3	18
4	24	4	24
5	30	5	30

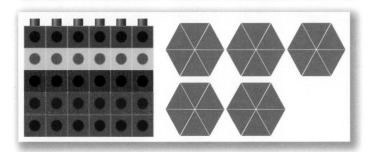

2 Using Tables and Graphs Using tables to represent change

Math Focus Points

◆ Connecting numbers in a table to the situation they represent

◆ Using conventional language for a table and its parts: rows, columns

◆ Describing the pattern in the numbers in a column and interpreting the pattern in terms of the situation the table represents

◆ Describing what is the same about situations that look different but can be represented by the same table

◆ Describing how the two numbers in the row of a table are connected to the situation the table represents

◆ Using information in a table to determine the relationship between two quantities

Tables are introduced and used as a central representation in this unit. Tables are a particularly powerful representation to show how one quantity changes in relation to another. Organizing data in a table can help students uncover a rule that governs that relationship (For example, for every increase of one for one quantity, the other quantity increases by three, as is the case for the total number of triangles needed to cover a certain number of trapezoids in the pattern block set).

Looking down the columns of this table, we can see how each quantity increases by equal groups: for every increase of one trapezoid, the number of triangles increases by three. By looking across the rows of the table, we can see how the constant ratio relationship of 1:3 is embodied in different pairs of numbers: one trapezoid can be covered by three triangles, two trapezoids can be covered by six triangles, three trapezoids can be covered by nine triangles, and so forth.

3 Number Sequences Constructing, describing, and extending number sequences with constant increments generated by various contexts

Math Focus Points

◆ Extending a repeating pattern

◆ Identifying the unit of a repeating pattern

◆ Creating a repeating pattern that has the same structure as, but different elements than, another repeating pattern (e.g., a red–blue pattern and a clap–tap head pattern)

◆ Defining even and odd numbers

◆ Determining and describing the number sequence associated with one of the elements in an AB, ABC, ABCD, or AABBC repeating pattern (e.g., 2, 4, 6, 8, . . .; 3, 6, 9, . . . ; 1, 4, 7, . . .)

◆ Determining the element of a repeating pattern associated with a particular counting number in AB, ABC, ABCD, or AABBC patterns (e.g., what color is the 8th element in a red–blue repeating pattern?)

◆ Determining how and why the same number sequence can be generated by different contexts

Associating the counting numbers with the elements of a repeating pattern reveals important characteristics of the pattern and also provides an avenue into studying the number sequences themselves. For example, we can write the counting numbers, starting with 1, under each element of a repeating shape pattern, like this:

Using the counting numbers in this way gives us a language to talk about the pattern.

• Triangles are on the "counting by three" numbers, or the multiples of three. To find the position of the next triangle, count on or add on three to the last triangle.

• The squares land on the numbers 1, 4, 7, 10, and so forth. Where will the next square be? To find its position, you also count on or add on three to the position of the last square. These numbers are not multiples of three, but they are one more (or two less) than multiples of three.

As students explore two-element and three-element repeating patterns, they encounter the odd number sequence, the even number sequence, and three different "counting by 3" sequences: 3, 6, 9, . . . ; 1, 4, 7, . . . ; and 2, 5, 8, ... In the example below, the numbers for the orange squares give the 2, 5, 8, . . . sequence.

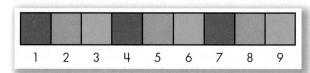

Much of the work on repeating patterns in Investigation 2 is focused on multiples of 2, 3, 4, and 5. These are the same number sequences that students encountered in the ratio work of Investigation 1. For example, as they consider the numbers associated with the last element of the unit in a five-element pattern, they generate the multiples of five.

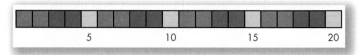

An important part of students' work throughout this unit is considering how and why different situations generate the same number sequence. For example, a cube building with five rooms per floor generates the same "counting by 5s" or "adding 5s" sequence for the total number of rooms column in the table below, as the sequence generated by the numbers associated with the yellow squares in the repeating pattern above.

Total Number of Floors	Total Number of Rooms
1	5
2	10
3	15
4	20

This Unit also focuses on

◆ Counting by and adding equal groups, such as 2s and 5s

Classroom Routines focus on

◆ Generating equivalent expressions for a number

◆ Developing fluency with addition and subtraction

◆ Using standard notation ($+$, $-$, $=$) to record expressions and write equations

◆ Using clocks as tools for keeping track of and measuring time

◆ Naming, notating, and telling time to the hour, half hour, and quarter hour on digital and analog clocks

◆ Determining what time it will be when given start and elapsed times that are multiples of 15 minutes

◆ Developing and analyzing visual images for quantities

◆ Combining groups of 10s and 1s

◆ Identifying coins and their values

◆ Adding coin amounts

◆ Using standard notation (¢, $+$, $=$) to write equations

◆ Using ratio relationships to solve problems

◆ Making estimates based on data collected over time

◆ Collecting, counting, representing, discussing, interpreting, and comparing data

◆ Counting by groups

◆ Counting a quantity in more than one way

◆ Using known combinations (e.g., combinations that make 10) to combine numbers

◆ Developing strategies for solving addition problems with many addends

◆ Using a place-value model to represent a number as 10s and 1s

◆ Recognizing that the first digit of a 2-digit number designates the number of groups of 10 and the second digit designates the number of ones

LOOKING FORWARD

Later this year, students again work with ratios as they work with money in *How Many Tens? How Many Ones?* (how many nickels in 25¢? 50¢?), and with odd and even numbers in *Partners, Teams, and Paper Clips.* As students move through the Patterns, Functions, and Change units in Grades 3 and 4, they will study more situations with a constant rate of change. In Grade 5, they will encounter situations that involve functions that are not linear. Tables will continue to be an important representation for recording and analyzing change. In Grade 3, students will continue using tables and will also learn to use line graphs to represent the relationship between two quantities. In Grade 3, students will use tables and graphs to develop rules (and, in Grade 4, equations) that describe the relationship between two quantities for any values in situations with a constant rate of change.

Assessment

ONGOING ASSESSMENT: Observing Students at Work

The following sessions provide **Ongoing Assessment: Observing Students at Work** opportunities:

- **Session 1.1, p. 32**
- **Session 1.2, p. 41**
- **Session 1.3, pp. 45–46 and 51**
- **Session 1.4, pp. 54, 57, and 58**
- **Session 1.5, pp. 63 and 66**
- **Session 2.1, pp. 79 and 81**
- **Session 2.2, p. 87**
- **Session 2.3, p. 93**
- **Session 2.4, p. 98**

WRITING OPPORTUNITIES

The following sessions have **writing** opportunities for students to explain their mathematical thinking:

- **Session 1.5, p. 67**
  Student Activity Book, pp. 31–32
- **Session 2.1, p. 80**
  Student Activity Book, p. 38
- **Session 2.2, p. 85**
  Student Activity Book, pp. 40–41
- **Session 2.3, p. 93**
  Student Activity Book, p. 45
- **Session 2.4, p. 98**
  Student Activity Book, p. 49
- **Session 2.5, pp. 102–103**
  M15–M17, End-of-Unit Assessment

PORTFOLIO OPPORTUNITIES

The following sessions have work appropriate for a **portfolio:**

- **Session 1.2, pp. 40–41**
  Student Activity Book, pp. 3–4
- **Session 1.3, p. 45**
  Student Activity Book, pp. 6–7
- **Session 1.5, pp. 64–67**
  Student Activity Book, pp. 25–32
- **Session 2.2, p. 85**
  Student Activity Book, pp. 40–41
- **Session 2.3, p. 89**
  Today's Number
- **Session 2.5, pp. 102–103**
  M14–M17, End-of-Unit Assessment

Assessing the Benchmarks

Observing students as they engage in conversation about their ideas is a primary means to assess their mathematical understanding. Consider all of your students' work, not just the written assessments. See the chart below for suggestions about key activities to observe.

See the **Differentiation and Intervention Guide** for quizzes that can be used after each Investigation.

Benchmarks in This Unit	Key Activities to Observe	Assessment
1. Explain what the numbers in a table represent in a constant ratio situation (involving ratios of 1:2, 1:3, 1:4, 1:5, and 1:6).	**Sessions 1.4, 1.5, and 1.6:** Floor Plans **Sessions 1.5 and 1.6:** Mystery Shapes	**Session 1.4 Assessment Activity:** Understanding Tables ✓ **Session 2.5 End-of-Unit Assessment:** The Nickel Jar (Problem 1)
2. Complete and extend a table to match a situation involving a constant ratio.	**Sessions 1.2 and 1.3:** Cube Outlines and Tables **Session 1.5:** Covering Hexagons	**Session 2.5 End-of-Unit Assessment:** The Nickel Jar (Problem 1)
3. Extend a repeating pattern and determine what element of the pattern will be in a particular position (e.g., the 16th position) if the pattern keeps going.	**Session 2.2:** A 3-Element Pattern **Session 2.3:** A 5-Element Pattern	**Session 2.5 End-of-Unit Assessment:** Shape Patterns (Problem 2)

 Checklist Available

Relating the Mathematical Emphases to the Benchmarks

Mathematical Emphases	Benchmarks
Linear Relationships Describing and representing ratios	1 and 2
Using Tables and Graphs Using tables to represent change	1 and 2
Number Sequences Constructing, describing, and extending number sequences with constant increments generated by various contexts	3

Algebra Connections

IN THIS UNIT

This essay is intended to illustrate how the ideas your students engage with in this unit lay the foundation for algebra. Second graders can and do think algebraically. Part of the work of this unit is helping students learn to verbalize those thoughts. Such skills will provide the basis for making sense of algebraic notation when it is introduced in Grade 4. Consider the following vignette from a class working on Investigation 1, Session 6 of this unit:

In this second-grade class, students are comparing two tables. One shows the relationship between the number of floors and the number of rooms in a cube building with 3 rooms per floor. The other shows the relationship between the number of hexagon pattern block shapes and the number of blue rhombus pattern blocks needed to cover the hexagons. Students are gathered on the rug, where there is also a model of the 3-room cube building with five floors and a set of three hexagons, each hexagon covered with a layer of three blue rhombuses.

Henry: When you use the cubes, it's like you're using something different than the blocks because, like, you're using different shapes.

Katrina: It's like that because they both have three to build. A hexagon needs three rhombuses. And a building has three in each one, so they're the same.

Melissa: This has three but it's going tall [pointing to the cube building], and this [pointing to the pattern blocks] has three and they're going this way.

Katrina then stacks three cubes on top of each of the hexagon/rhombus stacks. There are several audible "oh"s in the room.

Lonzell: I never thought of that!

Katrina: The rooms can be like rhombuses.

Total Number of Floors	Total Number of Rooms
1	3
2	6
3	9
4	12
5	15

Total Number of Hexagons	Total Number of Rhombuses
1	3
2	6
3	9
4	12
5	15

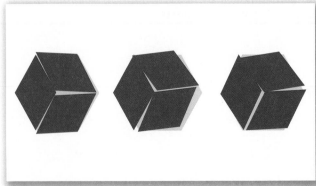

In this classroom discussion, students are noticing important similarities underlying two situations that look quite different. The number of rooms per floor and the number of rhombuses per hexagon, like many other familiar contexts involving equal groups, are actually ratio situations. Students know about sharing situations in which there are a certain number of something for each person, for example, two pencils per student, or situations involving packaging, for example, 12 eggs in a carton. In these situations, every time one quantity increases by one, the other quantity increases by the same amount. There are two pencils for one student, four pencils for two students, six pencils for three students, and so forth. For each additional student, the total number of pencils increases by two. This two-to-one ratio, which can be written 2:1, is evident in all of these number pairs: when there are six pencils for three students or 100 pencils for 50 students, the ratio is still 2 to 1, two pencils for each student.

In the classroom conversation above, students are considering two situations in which the ratio of two quantities is 3:1—three rooms per floor, three rhombuses per hexagon. Although students are not using the word *ratio* or the notation for it, they are describing and representing situations in which a constant increase in one quantity is related to a constant increase in another throughout this Investigation. When Katrina says, "the rooms can be like rhombuses," she is noticing that the ratio in two different situations is the same. As we see above, the tables of the two situations look the same. Describing the situations in words, we might say:

The total number of rooms equals the total number of floors multiplied by 3.

The total number of rhombuses equals the total number of hexagons multiplied by 3.

These situations can also be described using algebraic notation. Both of these situations can be captured by the equation:

$$y = 3x$$

where x stands for the total number of floors (or hexagons) and y stands for the total number of rooms (or rhombuses). [Note: in these situations, x can only be a whole number, since rooms and pattern blocks can only be whole numbers. In a different situation, $y = 3x$ might be true for any values of x, including fractions and negative numbers.]

If we graph each pair of values, the points fall in a straight line, showing the constant rate of change: as the number of floors (or hexagons) increases by 1, the total number of rooms (or rhombuses) increases by 3.

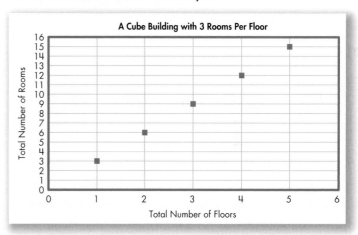

A Cube Building with 3 Rooms Per Floor

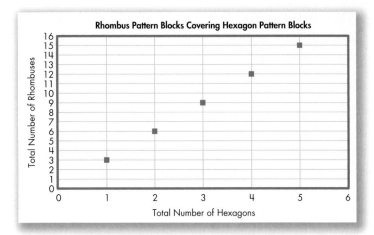

In Investigation 2 of this unit, students encounter repeating patterns that also have underlying relationships of a constant rate of change, but not all of them are ratios. For example, in the pattern below, the position of the black squares in the counting sequence is 1, 4, 7, 10, 13, 16.

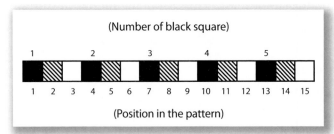

The number of each black square (1st black square, 2nd black square, 3rd black square) is related to its position in the entire sequence (1, 4, 7, 10, . . .). For example,

1st black square is numbered 1 in the sequence
2nd black square is numbered 4 in the sequence
3rd black square is numbered 7 in the sentence
4th black square is numbered 10 in the sentence

Here is a table for this relationship:

Number of Black Square (x)	Position of Black Square in the Pattern (y)
1	1
2	4
3	7
4	10
5	13

Compare this table to the ones showing the floors/rooms and hexagons/rhombuses relationships. In this table, too, for every increase of 1 in the first column, there is an increase of 3 in the second column. However, this relationship is not completely described by a ratio because one quantity cannot be found by simply multiplying the other quantity by some number, as was true for rooms and rhombuses. An equation that captures the relationship in this situation is:

$$y = 3x - 2$$

where x is the number of the black square and y is its position in the sequence.

Another way to look at this relationship is to graph each pair of values:

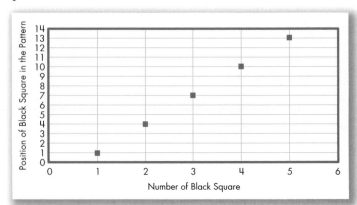

The graphs are helpful in providing a visual representation of why such relationships are called *linear* (students will use such graphs beginning in Grade 3). In all these instances, this constant rate of change results in points that fall in a straight line. In a ratio situation (rooms and rhombuses), this line, if extended, goes through (0, 0). The idea of a linear relationship, or linear function, is a central concept in mathematics.

For most adults, notation (the use of variables, operations, and equal signs) is the chief identifying feature of algebra.

The notation expresses in equations rules satisfied by particular pairs of quantities. Students in Grade 2 find, represent, and describe such rules in their own way. They investigate linear relationships between quantities by constructing the relationships themselves with materials, by creating and inspecting tables that represent these situations, and by describing what they notice, as Katrina did: "A hexagon needs three rhombuses. And a building has three in each one, so they're the same." This *reasoning*—about what the mathematical relationship is—*not* the notation, is the central work of elementary students in algebra.

Classroom Routines

Classroom Routines offer practice and review of key concepts for this grade level. These daily activities, to be done in ten minutes outside of math class, occur in a regular rotation every 4–5 days. Specific directions for the day's routine are provided in each session. For the full description and variations of each classroom routine see *Implementing Investigations in Grade 2.*

Today's Number

Students use strips and singles to make *Today's Number* and discuss place value as they look for patterns in the combinations of 10s and 1s. They also generate *Today's Number* using coins and solve problems about *Today's Number* in which different parts are missing.

Math Focus Points

- Generating equivalent expressions for a number
- Developing fluency with addition and subtraction
- Using standard notation ($+$, $-$, $=$) to record expressions and write equations

Quick Images

Students compare images, each made from strips and singles. They locate the numbers on the number line and 100 chart. Students also identify coins and their values, figure out the total value of a set of coins, and use ratio relationships to determine the total number of shapes used to make a given number of hexagons.

Math Focus Points

- Developing and analyzing visual images for quantities
- Combining groups of 10s and 1s
- Identifying coins and their values
- Adding coin amounts
- Using standard notation ($\cent$, $+$, $=$) to write equations
- Using ratio relationships to solve problems

What Time Is It?

Students review the number of minutes in a half hour and practice setting and telling time to the hour, half hour, and quarter hour.

Math Focus Points

- Using clocks as tools for keeping track of and measuring time
- Naming, notating, and telling time to the hour, half hour, and quarter hour on digital and analog clocks
- Determining what time it will be when given start and elapsed times that are multiples of 15 minutes

How Many Pockets?

Small groups determine the total number of pockets they are wearing and represent that amount with cube towers organized in 10s and 1s. Students then calculate the total number of pockets in the class and compare it to the total number of cubes.

Math Focus Points

- Making estimates based on data collected over time
- Collecting, counting, representing, discussing, interpreting, and comparing data
- Counting by groups
- Counting a quantity in more than one way
- Using known combinations (e.g., combinations that make 10) to combine numbers
- Developing strategies for solving addition problems with many addends
- Using a place-value model to represent a number as 10s and 1s
- Recognizing that the first digit of a 2-digit number designates the number of groups of 10 and the second digit designates the number of ones

Practice and Review

Practice and review play a critical role in the *Investigations* program. The following components and features are available to provide regular reinforcement of key mathematical concepts and procedures.

Books	Features	In This Unit . . .
Curriculum Unit	**Classroom Routines** offer practice and review of key concepts for this grade level. These daily activities, to be done in ten minutes outside of math class, occur in a regular rotation every 4–5 days. Specific directions for the day's routine are provided in each session. For the full description and variations of each classroom routine see *Implementing Investigations in Grade 2*.	• **All sessions**
Student Activity Book	**Daily Practice** pages in the *Student Activity Book* provide one of three types of written practice: **reinforcement** of the content of the unit, **ongoing review,** or **enrichment** opportunities. Some Daily Practice pages will also have Ongoing Review items with multiple-choice problems similar to those on standardized tests.	• **All sessions**
	Homework pages in the *Student Activity Book* are an extension of the work done in class. At times they help students prepare for upcoming activities.	• **Session 1.3** • **Session 1.6** • **Session 2.2** • **Session 2.4**
Student Math Handbook	**Math Words and Ideas** in the *Student Math Handbook* are pages that summarize key words and ideas. Most Words and Ideas pages have at least one exercise.	• **Student Math Handbook, pp. 37, 41–42, 93–103**
	Games pages are found in a section of the *Student Math Handbook*.	• **No games are introduced in this unit.**

Supporting the Range of Learners

The **Differentiation and Intervention Guide** provides Intervention, Extension, and Practice activities for use within each Investigation.

Sessions	1.1	1.2	1.3	1.4	1.5	2.1	2.2	2.3	2.5
Intervention	●	●	●	●	●	●	●	●	
Extension	●		●	●	●				
ELL	●	●					●		●

Intervention

Suggestions are made to support and engage students who are having difficulty with a particular idea, activity, or problem.

Extension

Suggestions are made to support and engage students who may finish early or may be ready for additional challenge.

English Language Learners (ELL)

English Language Learners need to know the rote counting sequence in order to construct, describe, and extend number sequences throughout this unit. They must also understand ordinal numbers, which are used to discuss tables (What does the *first* column tell us?) and repeating patterns (What color would go in the *tenth* square?).

You can emphasize ordinals in the context of various classroom activities. Esteban, you can be *first* in line today. Luis, go stand behind Esteban. You can be *second* in line. Students can practice saying ordinals in a variation on "counting off." We're going to count around the circle in a different way today. Instead of 1, 2, 3, . . . we're going to say *first, second, third, fourth,* and so on, until everyone has counted. You can post a chart in the room, listing the numerals 1–25 and their corresponding ordinals (e.g., 4 four, 4th fourth) for English Language Learners to refer to as needed.

The study of number patterns also presents opportunities to reinforce English Language Learners' understanding of *even* and *odd* numbers. You can use cubes to illustrate and review relevant concepts from Unit 3. I'm going to use cubes to make different numbers. Let's figure out whether each number is *even* or *odd.* Hold up one blue cube. Here's *one* cube. Does this cube have a *partner?* No, it doesn't have a partner—so one must be an *odd* number. Attach another blue cube to the first. Here are *two* cubes. Does each cube have a partner? Yes, these two cubes make a *pair,* so two must be an *even* number. Now add a green cube. Here are *three* cubes. Does each cube have a partner? No, this green cube is *left over,* so three must be an *odd* number. Have students continue extending the pattern with pairs of blue and green cubes, and help them determine whether each number is even or odd.

Working with the Range of Learners is a set of episodes written by teachers that focuses on meeting the needs of the range of learners in the classroom. In the first section, *Setting up the Mathematical Community,* teachers write about how they create a supportive and productive learning environment in their classrooms. In the next section, *Accommodations for Learning,* teachers focus on specific modifications they make to meet the needs of some of their learners. In the last section, *Language and Representation,* teachers share how they help students use representations and develop language to investigate and express mathematical ideas. The questions at the end of each case provide a starting point for your own reflection or for discussion with colleagues. See *Implementing Investigations in Grade 2* for this set of episodes.

Mathematical Emphases

Linear Relationships Describing and representing ratios

Math Focus Points

◆ Describing the relationship between two quantities in a constant ratio situation

◆ Using tables to represent the ratio relationship between two quantities

◆ Finding the value of one quantity in a constant ratio situation, given the value of the other

Using Tables and Graphs Using tables to represent change

Math Focus Points

◆ Connecting numbers in a table to the situation they represent

◆ Using conventional language for a table and its parts: rows, columns

◆ Describing the pattern in the numbers in a column and interpreting the pattern in terms of the situation the table represents

◆ Describing what is the same about situations that look different but can be represented by the same table

◆ Describing how the two numbers in the row of a table are connected to the situation the table represents

◆ Using information in a table to determine the relationship between two quantities

Growing Patterns: Ratio and Equal Groups

		Student Activity Book	Student Math Handbook	Professional Development: Read Ahead of Time	
SESSION 1.1	p. 28				
How Many Floors? How Many Rooms? Students construct cube buildings that have a constant ratio of "rooms" to "floors." They consider how to figure out the number of rooms when they know the number of floors.		1–2	96	• **Mathematics in This Unit,** p. 10	
SESSION 1.2	p. 37				
Using Tables to Record Students learn to use a table to record how the total number of rooms in their cube buildings changes in relation to the number of floors.		3–5	93, 94–95, 96, 97–98	• **Teacher Notes:** Equal Groups and Ratio, p. 105; Using and Interpreting Tables, p. 107 • **Dialogue Box:** "It's the Same Thing as Up There on the Table," p. 122	
SESSION 1.3	p. 44				
Comparing Tables After completing more cube buildings, students compare the buildings with a 1 × 4 and 2 × 2 floor plan. Students consider why the values in the tables for these two buildings are the same.		3–4, 6–10	96, 97–98	• **Teacher Note:** Using a Doubling Strategy to Reason About Ratios, p. 109	
SESSION 1.4	p. 53				
Assessment: Understanding Tables Students use partial information in a table to construct a cube building that matches the ratio relationship in the table and to fill in missing values in the table. Students are assessed on how they connect information in a table to the situation it represents.		3–4, 6–7, 11–23	94–95, 96, 97–98		

Classroom Routines See page 20 for an overview.

Quick Images
- Overhead Coin Set
- T38, Strips and Singles 🖥 Cut apart images into strips and singles.

Today's Number
- M11/T48, Today's Number 🖥 Make copies. (1 per student)

How Many Pockets?
- Connecting cubes

What Time Is It?
- Student clocks (1 per pair of students)
- Demonstration clock

Materials to Gather	Materials to Prepare
• **Connecting cubes** (20 per student)	• **M3, A Cube Building** Make copies. (as needed; optional) • **M1–M2, Family Letter** Make copies. (1 per student)
• **Connecting cubes** (30 per student)	• **Chart: "Building A"** Copy "Building A" table and floor plan from page 38 on chart paper. Keep this and all charts made for this investigation posted throughout the rest of the unit. • **Chart: "Building B"** Copy "Building B" table and floor plan from page 42 on chart paper and post.
• **T45, 5 Rooms on a Floor** 🖥 or paper divided into large squares • **Connecting cubes** (class set)	• **Chart: "Building C"** Copy "Building C" table and floor plan from page 47 on chart paper and post. • **Chart: "Building E"** Copy "Building E" table and floor plan from page 47 on chart paper and post. • **Chart: "Building I"** Copy "Building I" table page 49 on chart paper and post. • **Cube model of Building B** Make a model with connecting cubes that has 5 cubes in a line as 1 floor and is 3 floors high.
• **Connecting cubes** (class set)	• **M5–M6, Family Letter** Make copies. (1 per student) • **M7, Assessment Checklist: Understanding Tables** ✓ Make copies. • **Chart: "Building P"** Copy "Building P" table and floor plan from page 59 on chart paper and post.

🖥 Overhead Transparency   ✓ Checklist Available

Growing Patterns: Ratio and Equal Groups, *continued*

	Student Activity Book	Student Math Handbook	Professional Development: Read Ahead of Time	
SESSION 1.5 p. 61				
Ratio Relationships with Pattern Blocks Students use tables to represent ratio relationships between pattern block shapes and determine which pattern block relationships are represented by partially completed tables.	3–4, 6–7, 11–22, 24–33	96, 97–98, 99, 100	• **Dialogue Box:** Why Is It Counting by 3s? p. 124 • **Teacher Note:** Students' Difficulties With Mystery Shapes, p. 111	
SESSION 1.6 p. 69				
Ratio Relationships with Pattern Blocks, *continued* Students continue to work with tables to represent ratio relationships between pattern block shapes.	3–4, 6–7, 11–22, 25–32, 34–35	96, 97–98, 99, 100	• **Dialogue Box:** Comparing Tables, p. 125	

Materials to Gather	Materials to Prepare
• **T46–T47, Create a Building** 📇 (optional) • **Pattern blocks** (class set of hexagons, trapezoids, triangles, rhombuses) • **Connecting cubes** (20 per student)	• **M8–M9, Create a Building** Make copies. (as needed) • **Table: "Hexagon and Trapezoid"** Copy table on page 62 on chart paper and post. • **Table: "Mystery Shape 1"** Copy the table from *Student Activity Book* page 25 on chart paper and post.
• **M8–M9, Create a Building** (from Session 1.5; as needed) • **Connecting cubes** (20 per student) • **Pattern blocks** (as needed)	• **Table: "Hexagon and Rhombus"** Copy the first table from *Student Activity Book* page 24 on chart paper, fill in all numbers, and post. • **Table: "Hexagon and Triangle"** Copy the second table from *Student Activity Book* page 24 on chart paper, fill in all numbers, and post. • **Tables** Make sure all tables from previous work, with numbers filled in, are posted. See the list on pages 70–71.

📇 Overhead Transparency

How Many Floors?
How Many Rooms?

Math Focus Points

◆ Describing the relationship between two quantities in a constant ratio situation

Today's Plan		Materials
① ACTIVITY **Introducing Cube Buildings** 15 MIN · CLASS		• Connecting cubes
② ACTIVITY **How Many Rooms?** 25 MIN · INDIVIDUALS · PAIRS		• *Student Activity Book*, p. 1 • M3* (copies as needed; optional) • Connecting cubes
③ DISCUSSION **Sharing Solutions for 10 Floors** 20 MIN · CLASS		• *Student Activity Book*, p. 1 • Connecting cubes
④ SESSION FOLLOW-UP **Daily Practice**		• *Student Activity Book*, p. 2 • *Student Math Handbook*, p. 96 • M1–M2*, Family Letter

*See *Materials to Prepare*, p. 25.

Classroom Routines

Quick Images: Coins Using overhead coins, display three dimes and seven pennies. Organize the pennies into one row of five plus two. Follow the basic *Quick Images* activity. Ask students to focus on the type and number of coins they see as well as the value of the coins. When the coins are covered, ask students to explain how they determined how much money was displayed. Use equations to represent the problem and how students found the total. For example: $10¢ + 10¢ + 10¢ + 7¢ = 37¢$ or $10 + 10 + 10 = 30$ and $30 + 7 = 37$.

Repeat with five dimes and nine pennies in a row of five and a row of four.

ACTIVITY

① Introducing Cube Buildings

15 MIN | CLASS

Today we're starting a new math unit about different kinds of patterns called "How Many Floors? How Many Rooms?" In the first part of this unit, we'll be making buildings out of cubes and thinking about the number of rooms on each floor of the building. In the second part of the unit, we'll be working with repeating color patterns like red-blue-red-blue.

Take time to familiarize students with the idea that for this first activity, each cube represents a room in a building, and a group of cubes represents an entire floor of a building.❶

We're going to make buildings using these connecting cubes. Pretend that each cube is a room in a building. You can make a floor with two or more rooms. I'm going to make a floor with two rooms.

As students watch, connect two cubes of the same color. Using cubes of one color to make each floor can help some students see each floor as separate from the others. It is suggested that this strategy be used during whole class discussions.

This is one floor. You can make a building that is one floor, two floors, or more than two floors. I'm going to make a building that has three floors. For the buildings we'll be making, there is one rule. Each floor must have the same number of rooms and fit exactly over the one below it.

As students watch, add cubes to make a 3-floor building, with each floor comprised of two rooms.

Ask the following questions about the building:

• How many rooms are on each floor of my building?

• How many floors do I have?

• How many rooms are there altogether?

Teaching Note

❶ **Developing Common Vocabulary** It may take a while for both you and your students to become comfortable with the words *building, floor,* and *room* used in the context of the activities. Teachers have found that both they and their students sometimes said *floor* when they meant *room* and vice versa. Gentle reminders or rephrasing can help everyone get used to the language. Engaging students as collaborators in keeping the terms straight will also help to reinforce each word's meaning.

Teaching Note

❸ **Local References** Remind students of local buildings that contain more than one floor, such as an apartment building, an office tower, or even your own school.

Differentiation

❹ **English Language Learners** Students who are proficient in languages other than English can identify the rooms of the apartments in their first languages. You may want to show pictures of each type of room and have students identify them in English and in the other native languages represented in your class.

Take time to talk through what the cube buildings represent.❸ For example, hold up your cube "building" and say,

This is a building. Families of tiny people live in it.

Point to the first row of cubes and say,

The tiny Smith family lives on the first floor.

Point to each cube while identifying it.

This is the bedroom. This is the kitchen.❹

Explain that the tiny Diaz family lives on the second floor right above the tiny Smith family. Add the next row of cubes and say,

The tiny Diaz apartment is exactly the same size as the tiny Smith apartment.

Point to each of the cubes.

The tiny Diaz family has the same rooms as the tiny Smith family has—one bedroom and one kitchen.

Once students understand how the building is constructed, ask other questions.

- What if I built this building higher?
- How many rooms would there be if the building had five floors? eight floors?
- How do you know?

Depending on your students' facility with visualizing groups of two, you can have students construct buildings of different heights, or ask them to explain their thinking without actually building. Some teachers might find it more effective for students to just think about this first building without actually constructing it.

If some students are able to verbalize how they figured out the number of rooms for any floor, encourage them to talk about their ideas briefly. Keep in mind that this idea will be a focus of the discussion at the end of the session.

- [Rochelle], what's your idea about counting by 2s?
- Does anyone else have an idea about how you'd figure out the number of rooms if I told you a particular number of floors?
- Suppose I built it with ten floors, how many rooms would there be?
- How would you figure it out?

Construct a "floor" of a building made with three cubes in a row.

Now you're going to make a building that has three rooms on each floor, like this. Take a moment and make the first floor with a partner.

By making buildings with connecting cubes, students investigate the constant ratio relationship between number of rooms and number of floors.

Once everyone has made the first floor, ask:

If there are three rooms on one floor, how many rooms would there be if there are two floors? Build on another floor and show me what that would look like.

Make sure that everyone knows how to continue building on more floors with the same shape and number of cubes.

In the next activity, you're going to make five floors for this building. Then you're going to figure out how many rooms there would be if your building had ten floors.

Name _____ Date _____

How Many Floors? How Many Rooms?

A Cube Building

1. How many rooms does each floor have? _____

2. If the building has 5 floors, how many rooms are there in the whole building? _____

3. If the building has 10 floors, how many rooms are there in the whole building? _____

4. Show how you figured out how many rooms there are in 10 floors.

Session 1.1   Unit 5   1

▲ **Student Activity Book, p.1; Resource Masters, M3**

ACTIVITY

② How Many Rooms?

25 MIN   INDIVIDUALS   PAIRS

Students work on *Student Activity Book* page 1. They make a cube building five floors tall with three rooms on each floor and answer questions about it.

You can write something, draw something, or use numbers—whatever would show somebody who isn't in our room today how you solved the problem.

As you walk around, pick three or four representations for students to share in the upcoming discussion. Try to find solutions and representations that are different from one another.

ONGOING ASSESSMENT: Observing Students at Work

Students use what they can see about five floors of a cube building with three rooms per floor to figure out the total number of rooms for ten floors.

- **How do students represent their solutions?** Do they show the number of rooms on each floor, the total number of floors, and the total number of rooms?

- **Can students make connections between the cube building and their representations of it?**

- **How do students find the number of rooms in a building with ten floors?** Do they count on three for each floor? Do they skip count by 3s? Do they double the number of cubes in five floors?

As you observe students working, ask them what their representations show. Would someone else be able to understand it?

DIFFERENTIATION: Supporting the Range of Learners

Intervention For students who do not understand how the cubes represent "rooms" and "floors" of a building, continue talking through a story of the tiny people who live in the building. This is to help them visualize how each cube is a "room" and to help them relate these cube buildings to their own experience of buildings, floors, and rooms.

Intervention To help students see each floor as separate from the others, students might find it useful to use cubes of one color to make each floor of the building (e.g., first floor blue, second floor red, third floor yellow, and so on). This technique is not one that should be rigidly imposed.

Extension Students who easily build and solve problems about the three-cube building can build another building and represent it on A Cube Building (M3). Ask them to create a different floor plan using three to five cubes for a floor.

As students work with different numbers of rooms in a floor, new patterns emerge.

DISCUSSION
Sharing Solutions for 10 Floors

20 MIN   CLASS

Math Focus Points for Discussion

◆ Describing the relationship between two quantities in a constant ratio situation

Have students look at their completed *Student Activity Book* page 1.

Who can tell me something about how the building grows? What happens as each floor is added on? What else did you notice?

Students should see that as the number of floors increases, so does the number of rooms. Students might point out that they always increase by the same number.

Once they agree how many rooms there are in a 5-story building, go on to the 10-story building.

How many rooms are in a building with ten floors? How did you figure it out?

Students might say:

"The first floor is 3, the second is 4, 5, 6, the third is 7, 8, 9."

"I pointed to each floor and I said 3, 6, 9, 12, 15. Then I pointed to each one again because I needed 10 floors, and I kept going."

Other student approaches might include:

- Building ten floors and counting all the cubes

- Doubling the number of rooms for five floors

- Knowing that ten groups of three is 30

As students describe their solutions, ask them to share some of their representations for keeping track of the number of rooms on each floor.

When you were skip-counting by 3s or when you were adding on three for each floor, how did you keep track of how many 3s you needed?

Select three or four representations to talk about with the class. Choose representations that are different from one another and that bring out different features of the problem. If possible, sketch each of the students' representations on the board so that other students can see them.

Sample Student Work

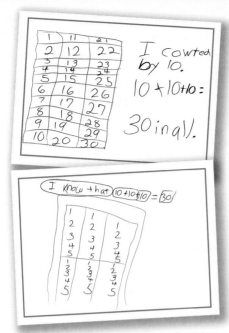

Sample Student Work

First we're going to look at [Henry's] representation. Who can explain what [Henry] did? What does his representation show?

With each representation, ask students what it shows. Also ask students what someone may not be able to tell from the representation. Follow-up questions might include the following:

• Can we see how many rooms we're adding for each floor?

• Can you tell the total number of floors?

• Can we see how many rooms are on the first floor?

• Can you tell the total number of rooms in the building?

• What if we wanted to know how many rooms are on the first three floors?

To close the discussion, ask students how their methods and representations would help them answer questions about a taller building.

If the people building this building now decided to make it 15 floors tall, could you use your method to help them figure out how many rooms they would have in the whole building? You don't need to tell me how many rooms it would be. I just want to know how you would figure it out.

Teaching Note

④ Types of Questions Teachers have found it useful to be explicit about the three different kinds of questions that students discuss in this unit and how the physical model of the cube building can be used to answer each. You may want to review these with students during this discussion and again in the next session.

- **How many floors are there?** [the number of rows or layers of cubes in the building]
- **How many rooms in one floor?** [the number of cubes in one layer]
- **How many total rooms?** [the number of cubes in the whole building]

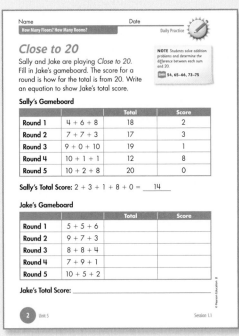

▲ **Student Activity Book, p. 2**

Some students may start articulating methods that would work for any number of floors. Encourage the class to keep thinking about a rule that would help them calculate the number of rooms for any size building.

So, [Leigh], your idea is that no matter what number of floors you want for this building, you could just keep adding on three that number of times? Any other ideas about this? We'll keep thinking about how to make rules for any number of floors as we make other buildings.④

SESSION FOLLOW-UP

④ Daily Practice

 Daily Practice: For ongoing review, have students complete *Student Activity Book* page 2.

 Family Letter: Send home copies of the Family Letter (M1–M2).

 Student Math Handbook: Students and families may use *Student Math Handbook* page 96 for reference and review. See pages 130–133 in the back of this unit.

Using Tables to Record

Math Focus Points

- Using tables to represent the ratio relationship between two quantities

- Connecting numbers in a table to the situation they represent

- Using conventional language for a table and its parts: rows, columns

- Finding the value of one quantity in a constant ratio situation, given the value of the other

Vocabulary

table
column
row

Today's Plan		Materials
ACTIVITY **①** **Introducing Tables**	🕐 15 MIN 👥 CLASS	• Connecting cubes; chart: "Building A"*
ACTIVITY **②** **Cube Outlines and Tables**	🕐 30 MIN 🧍 INDIVIDUALS 👥 PAIRS	• *Student Activity Book,* pp. 3–4 • Connecting cubes
DISCUSSION **③** **Ways to Find the Total Number of Rooms**	🕐 15 MIN 👥 CLASS	• Chart: "Building B"*
SESSION FOLLOW-UP **④** **Daily Practice**		• *Student Activity Book,* p. 5 • *Student Math Handbook,* pp. 93, 94–95, 96, 97–98

*See *Materials to Prepare,* p. 25.

Classroom Routines

Today's Number: 68 Using Strips and Singles Together as a class, use Strips and Singles (T38) to represent the number 68. Challenge the class to find all possible combinations. (There are seven if you include 0 strips and 68 singles.) List the combinations and discuss what students notice, paying particular attention to how the number of singles decreases by ten when a strip is added.

Professional Development

❶ Teacher Note: Equal Groups and Ratio, p. 105

❷ Teacher Note: Using and Interpreting Tables, p. 107

Differentiation

❸ English Language Learners To prepare English Language Learners to participate in this discussion, you can preview the terms *table, column,* and *row.* Some students will know that a table is a piece of furniture, so you may need to address the two different meanings of *table* in English. Right now we're sitting at one kind of *table.* Here's another kind of *table*; the word *table* has a different meaning in mathematics. Show students the table for Building A. We use this kind of table to record information. Every table is made of *columns* (run your finger down the columns) and *rows* (run your finger across the rows). This table has two columns and six rows. [Nadia], can you point to the left *column?* [Chen], can you point to the second *row?*

Stickers, Number Strings, and Story Problems

Stickers: Strips and Singles (page 1 of 2)

T38

▲ Transparencies, T38, M10

ACTIVITY

❶ Introducing Tables

This activity introduces the use of tables to represent situations in which there is a constant ratio between two quantities, as in the cube buildings students constructed in Session 1.1. Students will have several discussions that build on one another through the Investigation about how to use and interpret tables.❶ ❷ ❸

Show the "Building A" chart. If some students made representations in the last session that were similar to a table, remind them of the similarity.

Building A	
Total Number of Floors	Total Number of Rooms
1	3
2	6

This kind of representation is called a table. Who can tell me something about this table?

Help students read the headings of the two columns.

What are these numbers—1, 2—in the left column? What do they mean? How about these numbers—3, 6—in the other column? What do you think the table shows?

Students will probably recognize that this table can describe the 3-cube building they constructed yesterday. Next, use the connecting cubes to make a building with two three-cube floors. Direct students' attention to the building.

Using this cube building, who can show me what the 1 in the first column means? Who can show me what the 3 in the second column means? Can someone say a sentence about the building by looking at this row of the table? It says 1 in the first column and 3 in the second column. What do those numbers mean? Where can you see those numbers in the cube building?❹

As students work with tables, encourage them to keep making connections between the information in the table and the situation it represents and to articulate the connection between the two numbers in each row of the table.⑤

Now I'm going to add three more floors to the building, one at a time.

Ask students to tell you what should go in the table to represent those floors. Ask for sentences to describe one or two of these rows. Then use the connecting cubes to add a third floor to the building.

Now the building has three floors. I'm going to add three to the left column to show that I've added another floor. I'm going to add nine to the right column to show that now my building has a total of nine rooms.

Now I'm going to add the fourth floor. What number should go in the left column of the chart? What number should go in the other column?

Record students' responses on the chart. Then use the connecting cubes to add the fourth floor.

What does the 12 tell you? How can you see that on the building? Can someone say a sentence about the building by looking at this row of the table? It says 4 in the first column and 12 in the second column. What do those numbers mean? Where do you see those numbers in the cube building?

Draw students' attention to the row at the bottom that is separated from the rest of the table.

So far we have listed the total number of floors in order—one floor, two floors, three floors, and so on. But in the last class, I asked you to skip to ten floors and figure out the number of rooms. If we want to skip to a larger number without listing all the numbers in between, we use a separate row like this to show we've skipped some numbers.

Teaching Note

④ **Sentence Starters** You may want to provide a sentence starter such as the following to help students formulate their responses, "When I have one floor in the building. . . ."

Professional Development

⑤ **Dialogue Box:** "It's the Same Thing as Up There on the Table," p. 122

Building A

Total Number of Floors	Total Number of Rooms
1	3
2	6
3	9
4	12
5	15
10	

Teaching Note

⑥ Student Responses Some students may build each floor of the building and then count and record the number of rooms. Others might fill in the table by continuing number patterns they notice. Many students will construct at least five floors of each building, and all students should construct at least the first two floors of each cube building so that they can use it to explain the numbers in their tables.

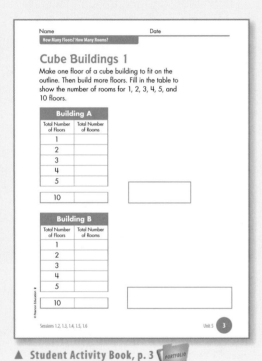

▲ Student Activity Book, p. 3

Another example of using a table to show a growing pattern can be found in the *Student Math Handbook,* pages 93–95.

The extra space means we've left some numbers out. What floors did we leave out of the table? What does the 10 in the first column of this bottom row mean? What should I put in the second column? How do you know? Can you say a sentence about this row of the table?

ACTIVITY

② Cube Outlines and Tables

30 MIN INDIVIDUALS PAIRS

Have students look at *Student Activity Book* page 3.

First you are going to make cube buildings that fit on each of the building outlines. Then you are going to fill in the table to show the total number of rooms for one, two, three, four, five, and ten floors. ⑥

Point out how the three-cube building fits on the outline of Building A.

What number would you fill in under "Total Number of Rooms" in the first row of the table?

Help students read a row or two of the table in terms of what it means (e.g., the numbers in the second row of the table mean that a building with 2 floors has 6 rooms).

After students complete *Student Activity Book* page 3, have them begin work on *Student Activity Book* page 4. Students will have more time to work on these pages and others in the next session.

Make sure that students can explain the numbers in their tables in terms of what is going on in the corresponding cube buildings. Making this connection is equally important for students who are less comfortable with number relationships (such as counting by 3s) and for students who are facile with numbers. Students who are less comfortable with adding on 3s can use the cube building to ground their thinking. Students who are facile with numbers may get lost in the numbers and lose their sense of how the numbers represent the changes in the building.

✓ ONGOING ASSESSMENT: Observing Students at Work

Students fill in tables that show the relationship between two quantities—the number of floors and the total number of rooms in their cube buildings.

- **Are students able to show or explain what each number in the table represents in the cube buildings?**

- **Do they notice a pattern in the rows and columns?**

- **Can students determine how many total rooms there will be when they add on the next floor?**

- **How do students figure out the number of rooms in ten floors?**

✱ DIFFERENTIATION: Supporting the Range of Learners

(Intervention) Encourage students who count the cubes by 1s without making use of equal groups to apply what they know about doubles. For example, they might start with 3 + 3.

(Intervention) If a student seems overwhelmed by all the numbers and lines in the table and is having trouble finding a way to focus, try isolating one row at a time using two sheets of paper to "frame" that row. Students can learn to use this technique for themselves.

(Intervention) Some students may find it beneficial to make each floor of the building with cubes of one color (e.g., first floor blue, second floor red, third floor yellow, and so on) to help them see each floor as separate from the others.

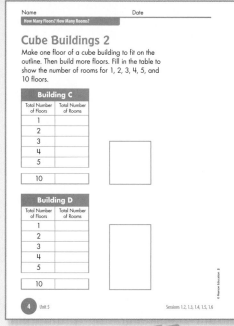

▲ **Student Activity Book, p. 4** PORTFOLIO

---

3 DISCUSSION

🕐 15 MIN 👥 CLASS

Ways to Find the Total Number of Rooms

Math Focus Points for Discussion

◈ Connecting numbers in a table to the situation they represent

◈ Finding the value of one quantity in a constant ratio situation, given the value of the other

The purpose of this discussion is to continue work on how a table represents the change of one quantity (total number of rooms) in relation to a change in another (total number of floors). In this discussion, students help you fill in the table for Building B, including a new column, "How I Figured It Out."

To begin, draw students' attention to the "Building B" chart.

Building B

Total Number of Floors	Total Number of Rooms	How I Figured It Out
1		
2		
3		
4		
5		
10		

Have students help you fill in the first two rows of the table. Then ask students how they thought about how many rooms there are in a building with two floors. Students may have counted by 5s or added 5s. Record their ideas in the third column, "How I Figured It Out."

Ask students to continue helping you fill in the table for three, four, and five floors. Ask students to explain their methods.

How did you figure out the number of rooms in the fourth row? Why did you add 15 and 5? Why did you add four 5s? How many 5s would you need to add when there are five floors?

Students' ideas for "How I Figured It Out" might include:

Building B

Total Number of Floors	Total Number of Rooms	How I Figured It Out
1	5	
2	10	5 + 5 5, 10
3	15	5 + 5 + 5 10 + 5
4	20	5 + 5 + 5 + 5 four 5s 5, 10, 15, 20 doubled 10
5		

10		

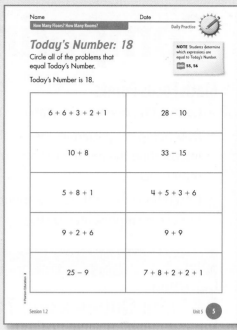

▲ Student Activity Book, p. 5

Finally, ask students how they figured out the total rooms for ten floors in Building B. Follow-up questions might include:

How many times would you need to add five for a 10-story building to find the total number of rooms? What other ways could you use to figure this out?

Keep the tables for Buildings A and B posted during the rest of the Investigation.

SESSION FOLLOW-UP
Daily Practice

 Daily Practice: For ongoing review, have students complete *Student Activity Book* page 5.

 Student Math Handbook: Students and families may use *Student Math Handbook* pages 93, 94–95, 96, 97–98 for reference and review. See pages 130–133 in the back of this unit.

Comparing Tables

Math Focus Points

◆ Connecting numbers in a table to the situation they represent

◆ Describing the pattern in the numbers in a column and interpreting the pattern in terms of the situation the table represents

◆ Describing what is the same about situations that look different but can be represented by the same table

Today's Plan		Materials
ACTIVITY ❶ **Cube Outlines and Tables**	30 MIN INDIVIDUALS PAIRS	• *Student Activity Book,* pp. 4, 6–7 • Connecting cubes
DISCUSSION ❷ **Comparing Tables**	15 MIN CLASS	• *Student Activity Book,* pp. 3–4, 6 • Chart: "Building C"*; chart: "Building E"*; connecting cubes (as needed)
ACTIVITY ❸ **Introducing Floor Plans**	15 MIN CLASS	• *Student Activity Book,* p. 8 • T45 🖳 or paper divided into large squares • Chart: "Building I"*; cube model of Building B*; connecting cubes
SESSION FOLLOW-UP ❹ **Daily Practice and Homework**		• *Student Activity Book,* pp. 9–10 • *Student Math Handbook,* pp. 96, 97–98

*See *Materials to Prepare,* p. 25.

Classroom Routines

What Time Is It?: What Time Will It Be? Write 3:30 on the board. Ask students to set their clocks to that time. Then ask:

• In 30 minutes, or one half hour, what time will it be?

Ask students to set the new time on their clocks and talk with their partner about what time it will be and how they know. Then ask them how that time would look on a digital clock (4:00). Repeat using half-hour intervals, varying the start times on the whole and half hours. Remind students of the work they did previously when they figured out that one half hour was the same as 30 minutes.

ACTIVITY

1 Cube Outlines and Tables

30 MIN · **INDIVIDUALS** · **PAIRS**

In this activity, students continue to work on making buildings that fit on an outline; figuring out the number of rooms in one, two, three, four, five, and ten floors; and recording their findings in a table. Students can finish *Student Activity Book* page 4, which they started in the last session, and then go on to work on *Student Activity Book* pages 6–7 as time permits. Students may work either by themselves or with a partner.

It is not necessary for every student to complete all the buildings. Encourage them to take their time building with the cubes, figuring out the number of rooms on each floor, and completing the tables. Explain that they can continue to work on their *Student Activity Book* pages during the next session. However, all students should complete Building C (the 2 × 2 building) on *Student Activity Book* page 4, and Building E (the 1 × 4 building) on *Student Activity Book* page 6 in preparation for the discussion in this session.

Students investigate the relationship between number of floors and total number of rooms as they construct cube buildings.

✓ ONGOING ASSESSMENT: Observing Students at Work

Students fill in tables that show the relationship between two quantities—the number of floors and the total number of rooms in their cube buildings.

- **Are students able to show or explain what each number in the table represents in the cube buildings?**

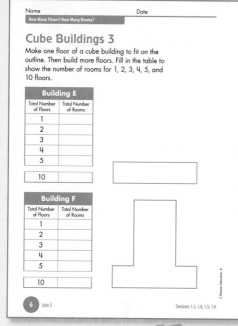

▲ **Student Activity Book, p. 6** *PORTFOLIO*

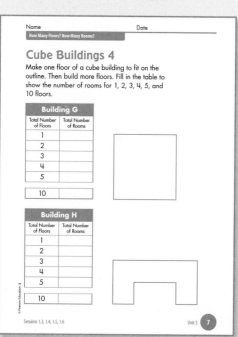

▲ **Student Activity Book, p. 7** *PORTFOLIO*

- **Can students explain what the numbers in one row of a table mean in terms of the cube building?**

- **Can students determine how many total rooms there will be when they add on the next floor?**

- **How do students figure out the number of rooms in ten floors?**

As students work, ask them to explain to you what one row of the table means, so they focus on relating the total number of floors to the total number of rooms (e.g., for 3 floors, there are 12 rooms).

DIFFERENTIATION: Supporting the Range of Learners

Intervention You can tailor the work to provide an appropriate level of challenge for each student. For example, if a student has difficulty adding 6s for Building D and needs to count by 1s, it may be enough for that student to complete the table only up to five floors.

Intervention If students are counting by 1s without using the structure of the building to help them (i.e., that each floor has an equal number of rooms), encourage them to use what they know about adding equal groups to give them a start toward finding the total. For example, most students know their doubles (3 + 3, 4 + 4, 6 + 6) and could add the number of rooms in two floors without counting by 1s.

Intervention If a student knows what to do but has difficulty keeping track of the numbers while counting on, provide a number line or a 100 chart that the student can use to keep track.

Extension For students who are facile with figuring out the number of rooms in ten floors for all the examples on the *Student Activity Book* pages, provide another number of floors for them to think about, (e.g., 12, 15, or 20 floors). For all students, continue to ask them to explain the numbers in their tables in terms of what is happening in the corresponding cube building.

---

15 MIN   CLASS

DISCUSSION

Comparing Tables

Math Focus Points for Discussion

◆ Describing what is the same about situations that look different but can be represented by the same table

◆ Describing the pattern in the numbers in a column and interpreting the pattern in terms of the situation the table represents

This discussion focuses on how situations that look different in some ways can be changing in the same way. In this case, the buildings look different, but the tables are the same. Point out the "Building C" and "Building E" charts that you have posted. Have students help you fill in the "Total Number of Rooms" column on the charts from the information they wrote in *Student Activity Book* pages 4 and 6. Encourage students to build the buildings as you are filling in the charts to help connect the values in the table to the buildings themselves.

Building C

Total Number of Floors	Total Number of Rooms	How I Figured It Out
1		
2		
3		
4		
5		
10		

Building E

Total Number of Floors	Total Number of Rooms	How I Figured It Out
1		
2		
3		
4		
5		
10		

If Building C has one floor, how many rooms does it have? What about when it has two floors? Can you determine how many rooms it will have when there are three floors? Four floors? Who notices a pattern? How would I figure out how many rooms there will be when there are ten floors?

Direct attention to the column, "How I Figured It Out."

What do you think should go in the column for two floors? Three floors? Four floors?

Many students will think of adding $4 + 4 + 4$. Make sure that the addition of equal amounts is shown for each row, since the repeated addition highlights the constant increase for each floor.

Some students might have some other strategies, such as doubling the number of rooms in two floors to get the number of rooms in four floors. You can record these strategies as well, for example, $8 + 8$ for four floors.❶

If some students are talking about figuring out the number of rooms as a certain number of equal groups, you might also write their language for this, such as, "three 4s."

At this point, some students have probably noticed that the tables for Buildings C and E look the same.

[Chen] pointed out that the tables for Buildings C and E look the same. What is the same about these buildings? What is different? Why do the tables have the same values in the second column? Building E looks something like Building B, so why aren't *those* tables the same?

ACTIVITY   15 MIN   CLASS

③ Introducing Floor Plans

The purpose of introducing the Floor Plans activity is to establish how to draw a floor plan for a building based on information in a table and to introduce partially filled-in tables that students will complete. Keep the introduction brief. Students will work on this activity in the next session.

In the Floor Plans activity, students construct a building based on the information in a table. Just like Buildings C and E, which have different floor plans but the same number of rooms per floor, the Floor Plans activity leads to different building configurations that result in the same table.

All students need to have connecting cubes available during this activity. To begin, show students the cube model of Building B.

Remember this building that we discussed yesterday? Who can tell me about it?

Take a few comments from students. Then show the "Building I" chart. Ask students to describe what they can tell about Building I by looking at the chart. Follow up with questions about the missing numbers in the chart.

Building I	
Total Number of Floors	Total Number of Rooms
1	5
	10
3	15
	20
5	
6	
10	

Here's a table about a cube building. It has some of the numbers filled in and some are left out. What can you tell me about the building that goes with this table?

Just by looking at the table, can you tell how many rooms there are when there is one floor? How do you know? Can you tell me what numbers should go in some of the blank spaces? What does the second row say? What does the 10 mean? What should the missing number in that row be? What does the second row tell you about the building?

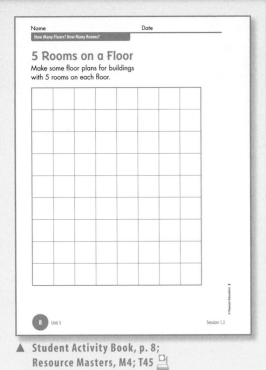

▲ **Student Activity Book, p. 8;**
   Resource Masters, M4; T45

Students will have noticed that this table can represent the model of Building B, with five rooms in a row for each floor. Now ask students whether another building could also match this table.

Here is the building you made with five rooms in a row on every floor. Is putting the cubes in a straight line the only way you could make a floor of a building with five rooms per floor? Remember, we just had two different buildings—the square building and the long building— that had four rooms on each floor. Could you put the cubes together in a different way but still have five rooms on each floor?

Take student suggestions for a different floor plan for a building with five cubes. Choose one that makes an L-shape. Using connecting cubes, hold up an example of the first floor of a cube building using the floor plan suggested by the student. Also, draw the two floor plans—the one row of cubes and the L-shape—on the transparency of 5 Rooms on a Floor (T45) or paper divided into large squares.

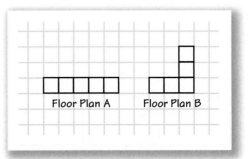

If we made a building from Floor Plan B—the one that [Melissa] suggested—what would it look like with two floors? How many rooms would there be with two floors? How many rooms would there be with three floors? Can you show me what the building would look like if it had three floors?

Have all students make the new building with at least three floors. Make sure that they know how to build on an identical floor to make the L-shaped building.

Then briefly refer back to the table.

Could our new building also go with this table? Why do you think so?

For the remainder of class time, have students make different buildings with five cubes per floor, each with a different floor plan. Have students record the floor plans for each of the buildings on *Student Activity Book* page 8.

Students can continue working on finding different floor plans for a building with five cubes per floor over the next few days. As students discover new floor plans, record them on the transparency or large-squared paper you began above.

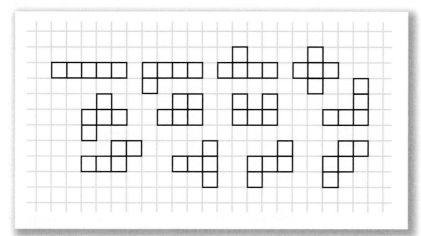

ONGOING ASSESSMENT: Observing Students at Work

Students find different floor plans for a building with five cubes per floor.

- **Do students understand that a floor plan is an outline of one floor of the building?**

- **Can students make buildings with non-rectangular floor plans, with every floor identical?**

Teaching Note

❷ **Pentominoes** Students may be interested to know that there are 12 possible one-layer floor plans that can be made by connecting five cubes (with reflections or rotations not counted as different shapes). These shapes are sometimes called *pentominoes*.

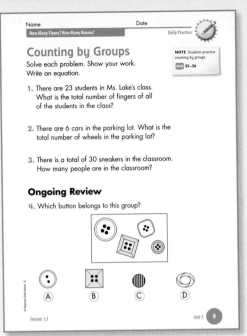

▲ **Student Activity Book, p. 9**

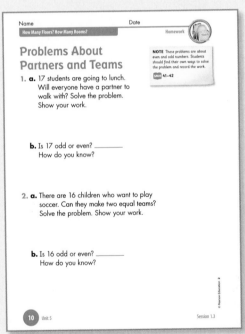

▲ **Student Activity Book, p. 10**

DIFFERENTIATION: Supporting the Range of Learners

Intervention Some students may find it easier to see and count the five rooms in the floor plan if they mark the squares on the grid with Xs first. Then they can draw an outline around the squares.

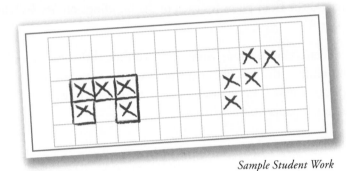

Sample Student Work

SESSION FOLLOW-UP

4 Daily Practice and Homework

Daily Practice: For reinforcement of this unit's content, have students complete *Student Activity Book* page 9.

Homework: On *Student Activity Book* page 10, students solve one problem about partners and one problem about teams. Based on their work, students determine if the number in each problem is even or odd.

Student Math Handbook: Students and families may use *Student Math Handbook* pages 96, 97–98 for reference and review. See pages 130–133 in the back of this unit.

Assessment: Understanding Tables

Math Focus Points

◆ Finding the value of one quantity in a constant ratio situation, given the value of the other

◆ Connecting numbers in a table to the situation they represent

◆ Describing how the two numbers in the row of a table are connected to the situation the table represents

Today's Plan		Materials
MATH WORKSHOP ❶ **Cube Buildings and Tables** ⓐ Cube Buildings ⓑ Floor Plans ⓒ Assessment: Understanding Tables	⏲ 45 MIN	ⓐ • *Student Activity Book,* pp. 4, 6–7 • Connecting cubes ⓑ • *Student Activity Book,* pp. 11–22 • Connecting cubes ⓒ • *Student Activity Book,* pp. 3–4, 6–7 • M7* ☑ • Connecting cubes
DISCUSSION ❷ **Making a Table**	⏲ 15 MIN 👥 CLASS	• Chart: "Building P"*; connecting cubes
SESSION FOLLOW-UP ❸ **Daily Practice**		• *Student Activity Book,* p. 23 • *Student Math Handbook,* pp. 94–95, 96, 97–98 • M5–M6, Family Letter*

*See *Materials to Prepare,* p. 25.

Classroom Routines

How Many Pockets?: Tens and Ones Groups of four to five students find the total number of pockets they are wearing and represent this amount with cube towers organized into tens and ones. Collect the pocket data by recording the number of pockets each group has on the board (e.g., 20 + 3 for 23 pockets). Collect the cube towers, and have a student double-check that the numbers recorded match the number of cubes from each group. After collecting the data, calculate the total number of pockets and compare it to the total number of cubes (e.g., 92 pockets compared to nine towers of 10 plus two extra cubes).

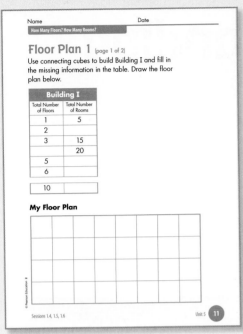

▲ Student Activity Book, p. 11

▲ Student Activity Book, p. 12

45 MIN

① Cube Buildings and Tables

In Math Workshop, students work on the two activities that have been introduced in this investigation: "Cube Buildings" and "Floor Plans." To begin, post the choices on the board and assign students to their first activity. In both activities, students work in pairs, but each student records on an individual page.

During Math Workshop in this and the next two sessions, carry out a quick individual assessment of each student, as described below in Activity 1C.

⒈Ⓐ Cube Buildings

PAIRS

Students continue working on *Student Activity Book* pages 4 and 6–7. Buildings F and H have nonrectangular "floors." Make sure that students know how to add on identical floors for these nonrectangular shapes. All students should construct the building and complete the table for Building F on *Student Activity Book* page 6 in order to be prepared for the discussion at the end of this session.

ONGOING ASSESSMENT: Observing Students at Work

Students fill in tables that show the relationship between two quantities—the number of floors and the total number of rooms in their cube buildings.

- **Are students able to show or explain what each number in the table represents in the cube buildings?**

- **Can students explain what the numbers in one row of a table mean in terms of the cube building?**

- **Can students determine how many total rooms there will be when they add on the next floor?**

- **How do students figure out the number of rooms in ten floors?**

DIFFERENTIATION: Supporting the Range of Learners

It is not necessary for all students to complete all buildings. You can tailor the work to provide a good level of challenge for each student.

Intervention If a student has difficulty adding 6s for Building D and needs to count by 1s, it may be enough for that student to complete the table up to five floors.

Extension For students who are facile with figuring out the number of rooms in ten floors for all the examples in the *Student Activity Book* pages, provide another number of floors for them to think about— 12, 15, or 20 floors.

1B Floor Plans

PAIRS

Students work on *Student Activity Book* pages 11–22. Students worked with Building I, the building on *Student Activity Book* pages 11–12, during the introduction in Session 1.3. However, students can benefit from constructing this cube building a second time and filling in the table themselves.

For each building, students should draw a floor plan of the building on the squares, fill in the table, and answer the question on the second page. They should also construct the building—at least several floors of it.

Help students understand what it means to draw the outline or *floor plan* of a building. Remind them of the outlines they used on *Student Activity Book* pages 3–4 and 6–7.

On those pages, each outline was a floor plan for the building described in the corresponding table. Now you are going to make your own floor plans.

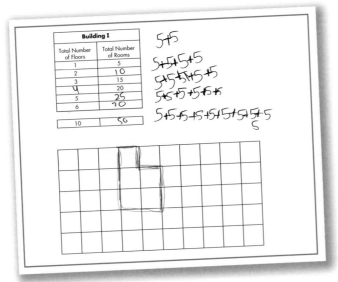

Sample Student Work

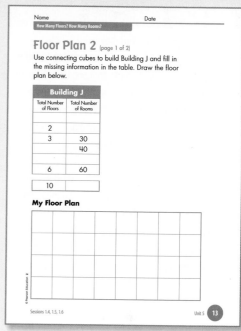

▲ **Student Activity Book, p. 13**

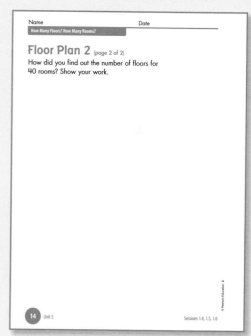

▲ **Student Activity Book, p. 14**

Teaching Note

❶ **Working Backward** You may need to help students figure out how to fill in a missing number in the first column. Students are used to finding the number of rooms (given the number of floors) but do not have experience in working backward—finding the number of floors from a given number of rooms. If students are having difficulty with this idea, make sure that they have established and drawn what the floor plan of the building is. Then have them build several floors of the building. For Building J on *Student Activity Book* pages 13–14, ask: How many rooms are on one floor of your building? On two floors? On three floors? So, if you keep building until you have 40 rooms, how many floors will you have? Try it out.

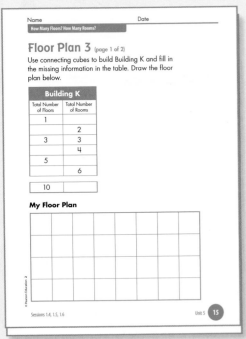

▲ **Student Activity Book, pp. 15–16**

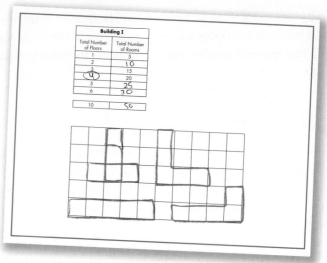

Sample Student Work

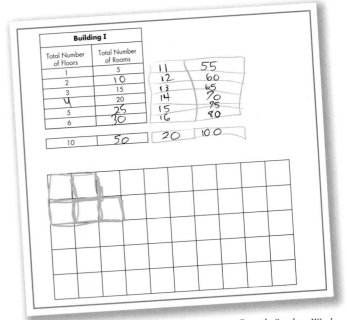

Sample Student Work

In these tables, the total number of floors jumps from six floors to ten floors, not from five floors to ten floors as on previous pages. Teachers have found that this change provides an opportunity to assess which students are paying careful attention to connecting the numbers in the table to their cube buildings.❶

ONGOING ASSESSMENT: Observing Students at Work

Students use a table to figure out the relationship between two quantities—the number of floors and the total number of rooms in a cube building.

- **Are students able to use information in a table to create a cube building?**

- **Can students explain what the numbers in one row of a table mean in terms of the cube building?**

- **Can students complete the table?** In particular, can they figure out the number of floors for a given number of rooms?

- **How do students figure out the number of rooms in ten floors?**

DIFFERENTIATION: Supporting the Range of Learners

Intervention As with the Cube Buildings activity, you can set different levels of challenge for students. All students need not complete all floor plans. It is more important for them to work carefully and thoroughly, constructing their buildings and checking that, for each example, the building and table match.

Intervention Students who are facile at doubling the number of rooms in five floors to find the number of rooms in ten floors—but have lost track of why they are doing this—may incorrectly double the number of rooms in six floors to find the number of rooms in ten floors. Help these students focus on what the numbers mean in terms of the cube buildings. For example, for Building J (*Student Activity Book* pages 13–14) ask:

How many floors do you have now for 60 rooms? How many more floors do you need to add on to your building to get to ten floors? What will happen if you double six floors? How many floors will you have then?

1C Assessment: Understanding Tables

INDIVIDUALS

Do this assessment as students work on the first two activities. It focuses on Benchmark 1: Explain what the numbers in a table represent in a constant ratio situation (involving ratios of 1:2, 1:3, 1:4, 1:5 and 1:6).

This benchmark will be assessed again at the end of the unit.

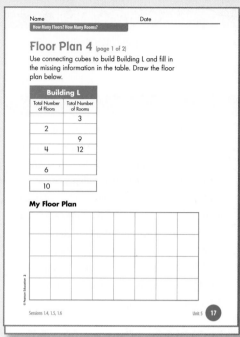

▲ **Student Activity Book, pp. 17–18**

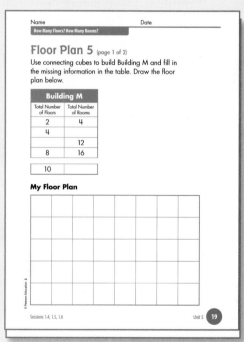

▲ **Student Activity Book, pp. 19–20**

Teaching Note

❸ **Out of Bounds** In order to carry out this assessment, you need to tell the students in your class that they are to work independently when you are talking to individual students. Some teachers tell students that they are "out of bounds" during this math period, because they are listening to and writing down each student's thinking. Carrying around a clipboard with the Assessment Checklist is a good strategy for reinforcing the message to students that you are not to be disturbed.

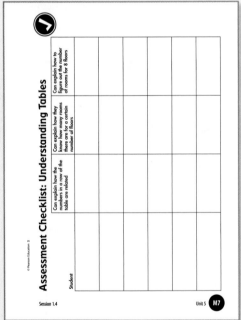

▲ Resource Masters, M7 ☑

Talk with each student about one of his or her completed charts on the *Student Activity Book* pages 3–4 and 6–7. Plan on spending two or three minutes with each student spread out over this and the next two sessions. This brief interview helps you assess students' understanding of the connection between the table and the cube building it represents.❷ Assessment Checklist: Understanding Tables (M7) is provided for you to record your observations as you question students.

To begin this assessment, choose a building on one of the *Student Activity Book* pages with numbers that are comfortable for that student. Ask each student to focus on one row of the table and explain to you what the values in that row mean. The student should show you with cubes or explain to you verbally how the numbers represent the relationships in a cube building. For example, in Building A on *Student Activity Book* page 3, row four shows that for four floors, there are 12 rooms, because there are three rooms on each floor, and $3 + 3 + 3 + 3 = 12$. Repeat this questioning for one other row in the table.

Then ask:

How could you figure out the number of rooms in the building if it had eight floors?

It is not necessary for the student to actually figure out the number of rooms for this assessment but to be able to say clearly *how* to get a solution (e.g., adding eight 3s or adding four more 3s to the number of rooms in four floors).❸

ONGOING ASSESSMENT: Observing Students at Work

Students explain what the information in a row of a table indicates about the cube building.

- **Do students know how the two numbers in a row of the table are related (e.g., there are 20 rooms in four floors of this building)?**

- **Can students explain how they know how many rooms there are for a certain number of floors in the table?**

- **Can students use their knowledge about how the building grows (i.e., the ratio of rooms to floors) to explain how to figure out the number of rooms for eight floors?**

DIFFERENTIATION: Supporting the Range of Learners

 As students continue to work on these activities, check in frequently with the students who need more support to help them make the connection between a number in a table and the number of floors or number of rooms in their buildings. These students may also benefit from making each floor of their building separately out of a different color block and then stacking the floors.

DISCUSSION

2 Making a Table

15 MIN   CLASS

Math Focus Points for Discussion

◆ Connecting numbers in a table to the situation they represent

◆ Finding the value of one quantity in a constant ratio situation, given the value of the other

During this discussion, students collaborate to fill in a blank table to represent a new cube building. They also talk more about strategies for finding the number of rooms for different numbers of floors in a building. Unlike the tables they have seen so far, no numbers are filled in on the table. Students will need to decide how to fill in both the Number of Floors column and the Number of Rooms column. Students should have connecting cubes available during this activity.

Point to the floor plan on the "Building P" chart.

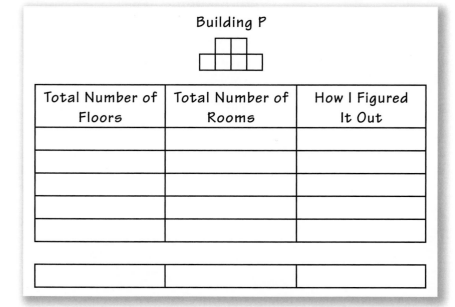

Building P

Total Number of Floors	Total Number of Rooms	How I Figured It Out

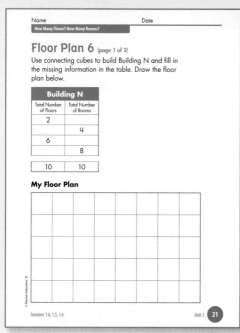

▲ Student Activity Book, p. 21

▲ Student Activity Book, p. 22

Professional Development

④ Dialogue Box: "It's the Same Thing as Up There on the Table," p. 122

⑤ Teacher Note: Using a Doubling Strategy to Reason About Ratios, p. 109

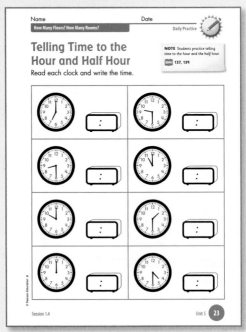

Name _____ Date _____

How Many Floors? How Many Rooms? Daily Practice

Telling Time to the Hour and Half Hour
Read each clock and write the time.

NOTE Students practice telling time to the hour and the half hour.
SMH 137, 139

Session 1.4 Unit 5 **23**

▲ **Student Activity Book, p. 23**

Here's a floor plan for a new building. What can you tell me about this building?

Have students help you fill in the table for Building P. Students can also construct the building out of cubes along with you. Follow up with questions about students' strategies for figuring out the total number of rooms. Record them in the "How I Figured It Out" column.④ ⑤

Continue to emphasize reading across a row. As needed, ask questions such as:

So what does this row show about the cube building? If there are five floors, what do you know?

Keep this chart posted during the rest of the investigation.

SESSION FOLLOW-UP

③ Daily Practice

 Daily Practice: For ongoing review, have students complete *Student Activity Book* page 23.

 Family Letter: Send home copies of the Family Letter (M5–M6).

 Student Math Handbook: Students and families may use *Student Math Handbook* pages 94–95, 96, 97–98 for reference and review. See pages 130–133 in the back of this unit.

Ratio Relationships with Pattern Blocks

Math Focus Points

◆ Using information in a table to determine the relationship between two quantities

◆ Describing how the two numbers in the row of a table are connected to the situation the table represents

◆ Describing what is the same about situations that look different but can be represented by the same table

Vocabulary	
triangle	trapezoid
hexagon	rhombus

Today's Plan		Materials
ACTIVITY **1 Covering Hexagons**	20 MIN INDIVIDUALS CLASS	• *Student Activity Book,* p. 24 • Table: "Hexagon and Trapezoid"*; pattern blocks
ACTIVITY **2 Introducing Mystery Shape**	20 MIN INDIVIDUALS CLASS	• *Student Activity Book,* p. 25 • Pattern blocks; Table: "Mystery Shape 1"*
MATH WORKSHOP **3 Mystery Shapes and Floor Plans** **3A** Mystery Shape **3B** Floor Plans **3C** Assessment: Understanding Tables	20 MIN	**3A** • *Student Activity Book,* pp. 25–32 • Pattern blocks **3B** • *Student Activity Book,* pp. 11–22 • M8–M9*/T46–T47 • Connecting cubes **3C** • *Student Activity Book,* pp. 3–4, 6–7 • M7 • Connecting cubes
SESSION FOLLOW-UP **4 Daily Practice**		• *Student Activity Book,* p. 33 • *Student Math Handbook,* pp. 96, 97–98, 99, 100

*See *Materials to Prepare,* p. 27.

Classroom Routines

Quick Images: Strips and Singles Using Strips and Singles (T38), display 56 with five strips and six singles. Follow the basic *Quick Images* activity. Have pairs discuss how they determined the number of squares. Repeat with the amounts 45, 34, and 23. As a class, find 56, 45, 34, and 23 on the number line and 100 chart and discuss how they are related.

ACTIVITY

Covering Hexagons

20 MIN · INDIVIDUALS · CLASS

Distribute pattern blocks to each group of students. Students should be familiar with these shapes from their work in *Shapes, Blocks, and Symmetry.* Four of the pattern block shapes are used in this Investigation: the hexagon, the trapezoid, the blue rhombus, and the triangle. You may want to review the shape names with your students.

Have students spend a few minutes finding out different ways to cover the hexagon with other blocks. Then show students the "Hexagon and Trapezoid" table you prepared.

Number of Hexagons	Number of Trapezoids	How I Figured It Out
1		
2		
3		
4		
5		
10		

Today we're going to cover hexagons with all one color. I see [Carla] and [Luis] covered their hexagons with trapezoids. So let's start with trapezoids. How many trapezoids do you think we need to cover one hexagon? What if we covered two hexagons with trapezoids? How many trapezoids would we need? How do you know? What about three hexagons?

Ask students to help you fill in the "Hexagon and Trapezoid" table.

Let's start with the first row. How many trapezoids did we need to cover one hexagon? The first row of the table says that for one hexagon, we need two trapezoids. What about for the second row? How many trapezoids for two hexagons? How did you figure that out? Who can say a sentence about the second row of the table, using their own words?

Continue filling out the table with the students, asking them to explain each row of the table in terms of the blocks. Record students' strategies in the third column.❶

How many trapezoids would you need to cover ten hexagons? How did you figure it out?

Have students work on *Student Activity Book* page 24, covering the hexagons and filling in the tables for rhombuses and triangles.

In this new context, students need to check that what they are writing in their tables makes sense in terms of the pattern block relationships. As with the cube buildings, making the connection between the numbers in the table and the blocks is equally important for students who are less comfortable with number relationships (such as counting by 3s) and for students who are facile with numbers.

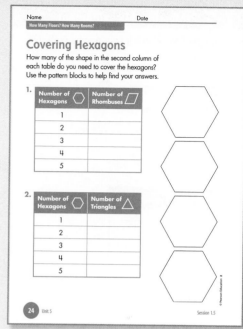

▲ **Student Activity Book, p. 24**

ONGOING ASSESSMENT: Observing Students at Work

Students determine how the total number of rhombuses or triangles used to cover hexagons increases as the number of hexagons increases. They represent this new ratio situation in a table.

- **Do students need to cover all of the hexagons with a given shape in order to fill in the table?**

- **Do students notice a pattern in the columns for total number of rhombuses and total number of triangles (increases by 3s and 6s)?** Can they explain why the numbers in the column increase in this way?

- **Can students explain what the numbers in one row of a table mean in terms of the pattern blocks?**

DIFFERENTIATION: Supporting the Range of Learners

Intervention Students who are less comfortable with adding on 3s can use the pattern blocks to ground their thinking. Students who are facile with numbers may get lost in the numbers and lose their sense of how the numbers represent the relationship of the two pattern block shapes. Check in with these students to make sure they can tell you what a row of the table means in terms of the blocks.

Extension Students who answer the questions easily and can explain how the numbers in the table represent a relationship between two shapes can figure out how many triangles or rhombuses would be needed to cover 15, 20, or 25 hexagons.

Professional Development

❷ **Dialogue Box:** Why Is It Counting by 3s? p. 124

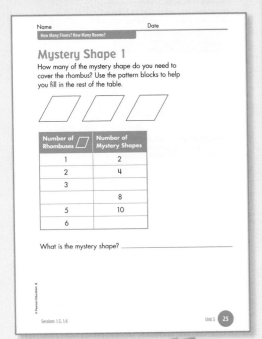

Name _____ Date _____
How Many Floors? How Many Rooms?

Mystery Shape 1

How many of the mystery shape do you need to cover the rhombus? Use the pattern blocks to help you fill in the rest of the table.

Number of Rhombuses	Number of Mystery Shapes
1	2
2	4
3	
	8
5	10
6	

What is the mystery shape? _____

Sessions 1.5, 1.6   Unit 5   25

▲ **Student Activity Book, p. 25** PORTFOLIO

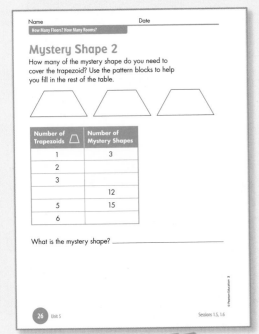

Name _____ Date _____
How Many Floors? How Many Rooms?

Mystery Shape 2

How many of the mystery shape do you need to cover the trapezoid? Use the pattern blocks to help you fill in the rest of the table.

Number of Trapezoids	Number of Mystery Shapes
1	3
2	
3	
	12
5	15
6	

What is the mystery shape? _____

26   Unit 5   Sessions 1.5, 1.6

▲ **Student Activity Book, p. 26** PORTFOLIO

20 MIN   INDIVIDUALS   CLASS

ACTIVITY
② Introducing Mystery Shape

Before introducing the Mystery Shape activity, you may want to have a brief discussion about one of the tables students worked on in Covering Hexagons. As in the work with cube buildings, emphasize the meaning of individual rows of the table. Also, if students notice the "counting by" patterns in the second column of the tables, ask them to describe what those patterns indicate about the pattern blocks.❷

To introduce Mystery Shapes, draw students' attention to the "Mystery Shape 1" table while students follow along on *Student Activity Book* page 25.

Here is a table about pattern blocks. This time you're going to be covering rhombuses. The table is about how many of one of the pattern blocks—the mystery shape—can cover the rhombus. Take a minute or two and see whether you can show with the pattern blocks what is going on in this table.

After a couple of minutes, ask:

If you think you know what the mystery shape is, don't say it yet. What do you notice about the numbers in the table? Can somebody say a sentence about the first row? What about the second row? How many of the mystery shapes should be in the third row?

Record students' sentences on the board. Now ask about the mystery shape.

Based on the information in the table and what you tried with pattern blocks, what do you think the mystery shape is? Do other people agree with this? Who can show with the pattern blocks why you agree or disagree? Can the mystery shape be anything else?

With students' help, fill in the missing values in the table. Students can fill in the table on their own *Student Activity Book* pages. On the chart, replace the heading in the second column with a new title, "Number of Triangles."

The Mystery Shape activity gives students a chance to think through how the values in a table represent the ratio relationship between two pattern block shapes.

MATH WORKSHOP

③ Mystery Shapes and Floor Plans

🕐 **20 MIN**

In Math Workshop, students work on Mystery Shape and Floor Plans. At the same time, you should complete the individual assessments you began in Session 1.4. Post the choices on the board, and assign students to their first activity. In both activities, students work in pairs, but each student records on an individual page.

③A Mystery Shape

👥 **PAIRS**

Students work on *Student Activity Book* pages 25–30. *Student Activity Book* pages 31–32 are optional. On each page, some students may fill in the table first and then guess the mystery shape. Others may try to identify the mystery shape first with the pattern blocks and then fill out the table.

Have students go through the pages in order. *Student Activity Book* pages 25–26 show outlines for pattern blocks along with the tables. *Student Activity Book* pages 27–28 provide only the tables, but students should still use the pattern blocks to show their answers. On these pages, the number of mystery shapes in the first row of the table is not given, so students have to figure out the number of the mystery shape that covers one block, using information found in the other rows.❸

❸ **Teacher Note:** Students' Difficulties with Mystery Shapes, p. 111

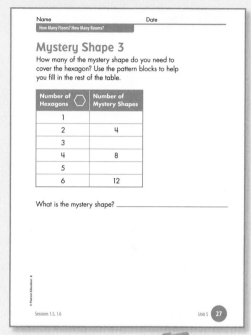

Name		Date

How Many Floors? How Many Rooms?

Mystery Shape 3

How many of the mystery shape do you need to cover the hexagon? Use the pattern blocks to help you fill in the rest of the table.

Number of Hexagons	Number of Mystery Shapes
1	
2	4
3	
4	8
5	
6	12

What is the mystery shape? _____

Sessions 1.5, 1.6

Unit 5 **27**

▲ **Student Activity Book, p. 27** PORTFOLIO

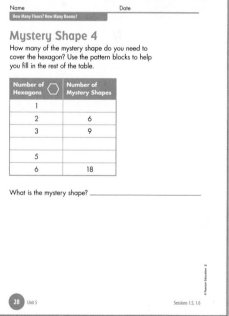

Name		Date

How Many Floors? How Many Rooms?

Mystery Shape 4

How many of the mystery shape do you need to cover the hexagon? Use the pattern blocks to help you fill in the rest of the table.

Number of Hexagons	Number of Mystery Shapes
1	
2	6
3	9
5	
6	18

What is the mystery shape? _____

28 Unit 5

Sessions 1.5, 1.6

▲ **Student Activity Book, p. 28** PORTFOLIO

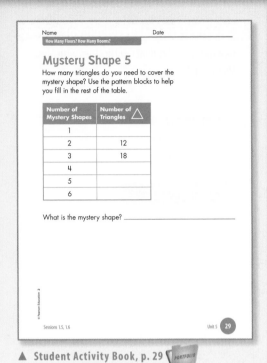

▲ Student Activity Book, p. 29

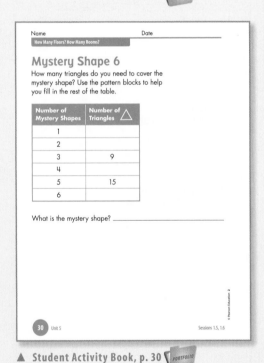

▲ Student Activity Book, p. 30

Student Activity Book pages 29–30 show the mystery shape in the first column instead of the second. This "backward" thinking may be difficult and unfamiliar at first. Expect to help most students reorient to thinking about the shape in the first column when they know the shape in the second column.

It is not necessary for all students to complete all the *Student Activity Book* pages. It is more important for students to proceed at their own pace and to carefully match what is happening with the pattern blocks to the numbers in the corresponding tables.

ONGOING ASSESSMENT: Observing Students at Work

Students fill in tables that represent the ratio relationships between pattern block shapes.

- **Are students connecting the pattern block relationships with the information in the table?**

- **Are students able to say a sentence about a row of the table?** Can they say what the numbers in each column refer to?

- **Can students identify the mystery shapes?** Can they describe how the relationship between the two shapes is shown in any row of the table?

DIFFERENTIATION: Supporting the Range of Learners

Intervention If students have difficulty with *Student Activity Book* pages 29–30, ask them to look back at one of the other tables they have completed and to say a sentence about one row of the table (e.g., "This row means that two hexagons can be covered by 12 triangles."). Then return to the example on *Student Activity Book* page 29 or 30 and ask:

What would the sentence be for this row? Can you say the same kind of sentence?

A student might respond by saying that three of this mystery shape can be covered by nine triangles. Encourage the student to put out the nine triangles and try to imagine how they could cover three of another shape.

Extension *Student Activity Book* pages 31–32 provide an additional challenge. On these pages, both columns are mystery shapes. The tables show a relationship students have seen before, but it can apply to more than one shape pairing. The first table has a ratio of 1:2, which can apply to the hexagons and trapezoids or to the rhombuses and triangles. The second table has a ratio of 1:3, which can apply to the hexagons and rhombuses or to the trapezoids and triangles. Students determine the identity of both shapes and consider alternate shape combinations. Then, at the bottom of the page, they draw the floor plan of a cube building that would have the same table.

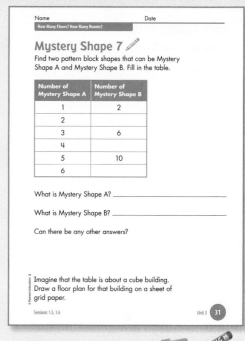

▲ **Student Activity Book, p. 31**

Number of Mystery Shape A	Number of Mystery Shape B
1	3
2	6
3	9
~~3~~ 4	12
5	15
6	18

What is Mystery Shape A? ___TraPeizond___

What is Mystery Shape B? ___Tringes___

Can there be any other answers?

Yes there a can be athnoer way Hexagon 3 rombas

Sample Student Work

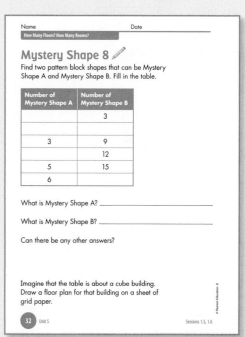

▲ **Student Activity Book, p. 32**

· ·

3B Floor Plans

PAIRS

For complete details about this activity, see Session 1.3, pages 48–52, and Session 1.4, pages 55–57.

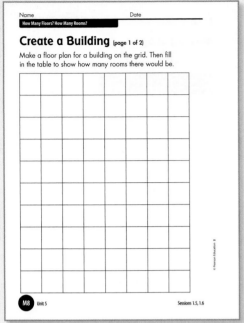

Name _____ Date _____
How Many Floors? How Many Rooms?

Create a Building (page 1 of 2)

Make a floor plan for a building on the grid. Then fill
in the table to show how many rooms there would be.

M8 Unit 5   Sessions 1.5, 1.6

▲ **Resource Masters, M8; T46**

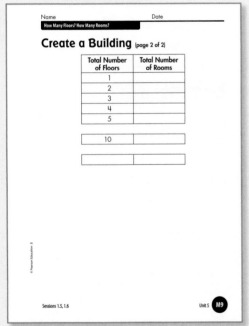

Name _____ Date _____
How Many Floors? How Many Rooms?

Create a Building (page 2 of 2)

Total Number of Floors	Total Number of Rooms
1	
2	
3	
4	
5	
10	

Sessions 1.5, 1.6   Unit 5 M9

▲ **Resource Masters, M9; T47**

DIFFERENTIATION: Supporting the Range of Learners

Extension Students who have finished *Student Activity Book*
pages 11–22 may enjoy devising their own floor plans, creating the
cube buildings for that floor plan, and creating tables to show how the
buildings grow on Create a Building (M8–M9/T46–T47), which provides
a blank floor plan grid and a blank table. The table includes an additional
row for more than ten floors. Students can challenge themselves to think
about how many rooms there would be for some larger number of
floors, such as 15 or 20.

3C Assessment: Understanding Tables   **INDIVIDUALS**

For complete details about this activity see Session 1.4, pages 57–59.

SESSION FOLLOW-UP

4 Daily Practice

Daily Practice: For ongoing review, have students complete
Student Activity Book page 33.

Student Math Handbook: Students and families may use
Student Math Handbook pages 96, 97–98, 99, 100 for reference
and review. See pages 130–133 in the back of this unit.

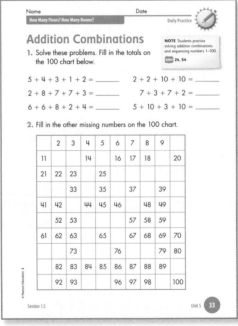

Name _____ Date _____
How Many Floors? How Many Rooms?   Daily Practice

Addition Combinations

NOTE Students practice
solving addition combinations
and sequencing numbers 1–100.
SMH 24, 54

1. Solve these problems. Fill in the totals on
the 100 chart below.

$5 + 4 + 3 + 1 + 2 =$ _____ $2 + 2 + 10 + 10 =$ _____

$2 + 8 + 7 + 7 + 3 =$ _____ $7 + 3 + 7 + 2 =$ _____

$6 + 6 + 8 + 2 + 4 =$ _____ $5 + 10 + 3 + 10 =$ _____

2. Fill in the other missing numbers on the 100 chart.

	2	3	4	5	6	7	8	9	
11			14		16	17	18		20
21	22	23		25					
		33		35		37		39	
41	42		44	45	46		48	49	
	52	53				57	58	59	
61	62	63		65		67	68	69	70
		73			76			79	80
	82	83	84	85	86	87	88	89	
	92	93			96	97	98		100

Session 1.5   Unit 5 33

▲ **Student Activity Book, p. 33**

Ratio Relationships with Pattern Blocks, *continued*

Math Focus Points

◆ Using information in a table to determine the relationship between two quantities

◆ Using tables to represent the ratio relationship between two quantities

◆ Describing what is the same about situations that look different but can be represented by the same table

Today's Plan		Materials
MATH WORKSHOP **① Mystery Shapes and Floor Plans** ⒜ Mystery Shape ⒝ Floor Plans ⒞ Assessment: Understanding Tables	40 MIN	⒜ • *Student Activity Book,* pp. 25–32 • Pattern blocks ⒝ • *Student Activity Book,* pp. 11–22 • M8–M9 ⒞ • *Student Activity Book,* pp. 3–4, 6–7 • M7 • Connecting cubes
DISCUSSION **② Comparing Tables**	20 MIN CLASS	• Table: "Hexagon and Rhombus"*; Table: "Hexagon and Triangle"*; pattern blocks (as needed)
SESSION FOLLOW-UP **③ Daily Practice and Homework**		• *Student Activity Book,* pp. 34–35 • *Student Math Handbook,* pp. 96, 97–98, 99, 100

*See *Materials to Prepare,* p. 27.

Classroom Routines

Today's Number: 25 with Missing Parts Each student completes *Today's Number: 25* (M11/T48). When they are finished they can compare answers with a partner. Select a couple of examples for students to discuss how they solved the problem.

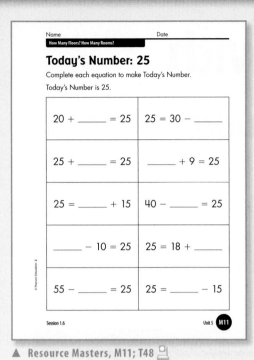

Name _____ Date _____

How Many Floors? How Many Rooms?

Today's Number: 25

Complete each equation to make Today's Number.

Today's Number is 25.

20 + _____ = 25	25 = 30 − _____
25 + _____ = 25	_____ + 9 = 25
25 = _____ + 15	40 − _____ = 25
_____ − 10 = 25	25 = 18 + _____
55 − _____ = 25	25 = _____ − 15

Session 1.6

Unit 5 M11

▲ Resource Masters, M11; T48

MATH WORKSHOP
① Mystery Shapes and Floor Plans

40 MIN

In Math Workshop, students work on two activities: Mystery Shape and Floor Plans. In addition, you should complete the individual assessment you began in Session 1.4. Post the choices on the board and assign students to their first activity. In both activities, students work in pairs, but each student records on individual pages.

1A Mystery Shape

PAIRS

For complete details about this activity, see Session 1.5, pages 64–67.

1B Floor Plans

PAIRS

For complete details about this activity, see Session 1.3, pages 48–52, and Session 1.4, pages 55–57.

1C Assessment: Understanding Tables

INDIVIDUALS

For complete details about this activity, see Session 1.4, pages 57–59.

DISCUSSION
② Comparing Tables

20 MIN   CLASS

Math Focus Points for Discussion

◆ Describing what is the same about situations that look different but can be represented by the same table

For this discussion, post the two new tables you prepared, one for the hexagon and rhombus and one for the hexagon and triangle. Also, make sure that all the charts and tables you used in previous sessions are posted in the room where students can easily see them. You should have:

- "Building A" chart (a 1:3 relationship)
- "Building B" chart (a 1:5 relationship)
- "Building C" chart (a 1:4 relationship)
- "Building E" chart (a 1:4 relationship)
- "Building I" chart (a 1:5 relationship)

- "Building P" chart (a 1:6 relationship)

- Hexagon and Trapezoid table (a 1:2 relationship)

- Rhombus and Triangle table (originally "Mystery Shape 1") (a 1:2 relationship)

- Hexagon and Rhombus table (a 1:3 relationship)

- Hexagon and Triangle table (a 1:6 relationship)

Professional Development

❶ **Dialogue Box:** Comparing Tables, p. 125

The goal of this discussion is to have students think about why some tables that describe different contexts look the same. First they consider pattern block tables that have the same numbers; then they compare pattern block tables with cube building tables.❶ Point out the tables for Buildings C and E, which you discussed in Session 1.3. Even though the two buildings look different, the numbers in the tables are the same. Ask students to look at the tables posted around the room and see whether there are any other tables that look the same. After students have pointed out which are the same, focus their attention on the Hexagon and Trapezoid table and the Rhombus and Triangle table.

Why are the numbers in these two tables the same? We used different blocks. This one is about covering hexagons with trapezoids, but this one is about covering rhombuses with triangles. Who can explain it? Who has an idea?

As students give ideas, ask them to demonstrate what they are saying with pattern blocks (or use overhead pattern block pieces). If students make statements that involve only numbers, ask them what the numbers represent.

Students might say:

"They both have 2."

[Juanita], you said they both have two. What do you mean by that? In this table, what does this two mean? What about in this table? Can you show it with the pattern blocks?

Once students have talked about the 2-pattern block tables, turn to an example that students have noticed of a cube building table and a pattern block table that have the same numbers on them (e.g., Building A [three rooms per floor] and the Hexagon and Rhombus table [three rhombuses cover each hexagon]). Ask students why these two are the same.

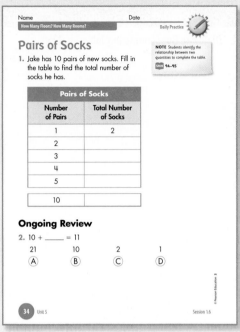

▲ **Student Activity Book, p. 34**

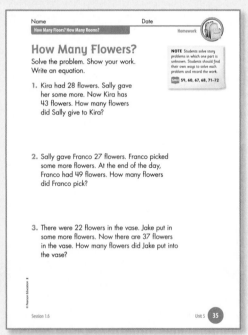

▲ **Student Activity Book, p. 35**

What about the tables for Building A and for the Hexagon and Rhombus? One table is about a cube building, and the other is about the pattern blocks. Why do the two tables look the same?

Students might say:

"When we have one floor, we have three rooms."

"And when we have one hexagon, we need three rhombuses."

After some discussion, summarize what students have been saying.

Even though we're talking about different things, each time we have one floor or one hexagon, we have three of something else—either rooms or rhombuses—that go with it.

If there is time, ask the class to pretend that the "Hexagon and Trapezoid" table is really describing a cube building. What could that building look like? What about the table for Building P (six rooms per floor)? Is there a pattern block table that is the same?

Keep all the tables from this Investigation posted during Investigation 2.

SESSION FOLLOW-UP

3 Daily Practice and Homework

Daily Practice: For reinforcement of this unit's content, have students complete *Student Activity Book* page 34.

Homework: On *Student Activity Book* page 35, students solve three story problems in which one part is unknown and record their thinking.

Student Math Handbook: Students and families may use *Student Math Handbook* pages 96, 97–98, 99, 100 for reference and review. See pages 130–133 in the back of this unit.

Mathematical Emphasis

Number Sequences Constructing, describing, and extending number sequences with constant increments generated by various contexts

Math Focus Points

◆ Extending a repeating pattern

◆ Identifying the unit of a repeating pattern

◆ Creating a repeating pattern that has the same structure as, but different elements than, another repeating pattern (e.g., a red–blue pattern and a clap–tap head pattern)

◆ Defining even and odd numbers

◆ Determining and describing the number sequence associated with one of the elements in an AB, ABC, ABCD, or AABBC repeating pattern (e.g., 2, 4, 6, 8, . . . ; 3, 6, 9, . . . ; 1, 4, 7, . . .)

◆ Determining the element of a repeating pattern associated with a particular counting number in AB, ABC, ABCD, or AABBC patterns (e.g., what color is the 8th element in a red–blue repeating pattern?)

◆ Determining how and why the same number sequence can be generated by different contexts

Repeating Patterns and Number Sequences

	Student Activity Book	Student Math Handbook	Professional Development: Read Ahead of Time	
SESSION 2.1 p. 76				
Cube Train Patterns Students construct and describe repeating patterns, using body movements and colored connecting cubes. They determine what colors are associated with certain numbers on a number strip.	37–39	101, 102, 103	• **Teacher Note:** Repeating Patterns, p. 113	
SESSION 2.2 p. 82				
Counting by 2s Students describe the number sequences associated with each color in their color patterns, including the even and odd number sequences. They use these number sequences to determine what comes in a particular position in the pattern.	38, 40–43	37, 41–42, 103	• **Dialogue Box:** "The Reds Are Uneven," p. 126	
SESSION 2.3 p. 89				
Counting by 3s The class discusses the number sequences associated with each color in their yellow–red–blue cube pattern: 3, 6, 9, . . . ; 1, 4, 7, . . . ; and 2, 5, 8, ... They construct and describe an AABBC pattern.	40–41, 45–46	103	• **Dialogue Box:** Counting by 3s, p. 128	
SESSION 2.4 p. 95				
How Is Red–Blue–Brown–Green Like Yellow–Black–White–Orange? The class discusses the number sequences associated with the last element in the units of 5-element (AABBC) and 4-element (ABCD) patterns. They compare two ABCD patterns made with different colors.	45, 47–51	101, 103		
SESSION 2.5 p. 101				
End-of-Unit Assessment Students work on two problems as an End-of-Unit Assessment, one that involves a new constant ratio situation, and one that involves repeating patterns and number sequences.	53	96, 97–98, 100, 103	• **Teacher Note:** End-of-Unit Assessment, p. 114	

Quick Images
- T49–T50, *Quick Images with Pattern Blocks 1* 🖥 (Images 1, 2, and 3)
- **Overhead coin set**

Today's Number
- **Class set of coins** (as needed)

What Time Is It?
- **Student clocks** (1 per pair of students)
- **Demonstration clock**

Materials to Gather	Materials to Prepare
• **Connecting cubes** (class set) • **Markers or crayons** (as needed) • **Red and blue markers or crayons** (1 of each per student) • **100 chart** (optional)	• **Cube trains** Prepare a 4-cube train of connecting cubes using 2 alternating colors, red–blue–red–blue. Prepare a 6-cube train using 3 alternating colors, yellow–blue–green–yellow–blue–green. • **Number strip** Prepare a number strip on chart paper like the one shown on page 80.
• **Connecting cubes** (yellows, reds, and blues) • **Chart paper** • **Yellow, red, and blue markers or crayons** (1 of each per student) • **Pocket 100 chart numbers** (optional)	
• **Chart paper** (as needed; optional) • **Connecting cubes** (yellows, greens, and oranges) • **Yellow, green, and orange markers or crayons** (1 of each color per student)	• **Number strip** On chart paper, draw and color a number strip with 9 boxes showing the repeating pattern yellow–red–blue as shown on page 90. • **"Blue Squares" table** On chart paper, draw a table showing the numbers for the blue squares in the yellow–red–blue pattern as shown on page 91.
• **Chart paper** (as needed; optional) • **Connecting cubes** (class set)	• **Number strips** Draw three number strips on separate sheets of chart paper: **1.** one with 10 boxes showing the repeating pattern yellow–yellow–green–green–orange; **2.** the second with 8 boxes showing the repeating pattern red–blue–brown–green; **3.** the third with 8 boxes showing the repeating pattern yellow–black–white–orange. • **"Green Squares" table** On chart paper, draw a table showing the numbers for the green squares in the red–blue–brown–green pattern, as shown on page 100.
	• **M14–M17, End-of-Unit Assessment** Make copies. (1 per student)

🖥 Overhead Transparency

Cube Train Patterns

Math Focus Points

◆ Extending a repeating pattern

◆ Identifying the unit of a repeating pattern

◆ Creating a repeating pattern that has the same structure as, but different elements than, another repeating pattern (e.g., a red–blue pattern and a clap–tap head pattern)

Vocabulary
repeating pattern
unit

Today's Plan		Materials
① DISCUSSION **Repeating Patterns** 20 MIN CLASS		• Cube trains*
② ACTIVITY **Make a Repeating Pattern** 15 MIN INDIVIDUALS		• *Student Activity Book,* p. 37 • Markers or crayons (as needed); connecting cubes
③ ACTIVITY **Introducing the Number Strip** 25 MIN PAIRS CLASS		• *Student Activity Book,* p. 38 • Number strip*; 4-cube train (from Activity 1); connecting cubes; red and blue markers or crayons; blank 100 chart (optional)
④ SESSION FOLLOW-UP **Daily Practice**		• *Student Activity Book,* p. 39 • *Student Math Handbook,* pp. 101, 102, 103

*See *Materials to Prepare,* p. 75.

Classroom Routines

What Time Is It? Students work together with a partner to practice setting their individual clocks to the quarter hour. One student suggests a time, and the other one sets the time. They take turns with these two roles. Pair students who are at similar levels of understanding.

DISCUSSION

1 Repeating Patterns

20 MIN   CLASS

Math Focus Points for Discussion

◆ Identifying the unit of a repeating pattern

◆ Creating a repeating pattern that has the same structure as, but different elements than, another repeating pattern (e.g., a red–blue pattern and a clap–tap head pattern)

This investigation begins with a review of repeating patterns—both color patterns and body movement patterns—such as the ones students worked with in the Grade 1 unit, *Color, Shape, and Number Patterns.*

Start the session with a body movement pattern. Body movement patterns involve repeating a series of simple physical actions, such as clapping hands, slapping knees, putting both hands on head, and so on. Begin by showing the class a two-element (AB) pattern—such as tap head–tap shoulders—and having students repeat the action with you. Then stop the action, keeping your hands at the last position, and ask the class what action comes next. Repeat the procedure with another two-element pattern and then with a three-element (ABC) pattern, such as slap knees–slap knees–clap.

In this investigation we're going to be working with repeating patterns. We just did a few body movement patterns. In this pattern [show one of those you just did, such as tap head–tap shoulders], what's the part that repeats over and over?

Help students identify the unit of the pattern—tap head–tap shoulders—and remind them of the word *unit.*❶ Next, hold up the train of four cubes you prepared with two alternating colors.

Here's a repeating pattern I've started with the cubes. What do you notice? If the pattern keeps going in the same way, what color should come next? Now what color cube should I put on?❷

Keep building the train until, alternating the two colors, you have eight cubes.

Professional Development
❶ **Teacher Note:** Repeating Patterns, p. 113

Teaching Note
❷ **Student Responses** Sometimes students point out that a different color *could* come next. For example, the pattern might be red–blue–red–blue–green–red–blue–red–blue–green or any of many other possibilities. If a student brings up this important point, acknowledge it, and let the class know that although those ways to continue the pattern could also work, you *did* have the red–blue pattern in mind this time.

It may help students if you break the train into its separate units.

What's the <mark>unit</mark> of this pattern?

Finally, show the train of six cubes you prepared with three alternating colors.

What comes next?

Then add cubes to the train until you have 12 cubes total following the color pattern.

What is the *unit* of this pattern? [In this example, the unit would be yellow–blue–green.]

Show students the red–blue cube train again.

Can someone make a body movement pattern that matches this cube pattern?

Elicit some examples from the children such as clap–slap knees–clap–slap knees. If students do not understand the question, choose a 2-element movement pattern and say, "red, blue, red, blue," as you act out the pattern. As the students offer ideas, act out the student suggestions saying, "red, blue," to match the actions. Recording on the board may help some students make the connection between the color pattern and the movement pattern.

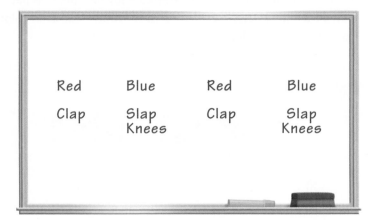

Repeat the procedure with a three-element pattern. Show the 3-element cube train, and ask the class to create a matching movement pattern. Ask,

How does our body movement pattern go with the cube train?

Again you may want to help students make the connection between the color and movement patterns by recording the following on the board:

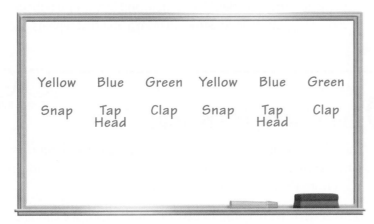

Yellow	Blue	Green	Yellow	Blue	Green
Snap	Tap Head	Clap	Snap	Tap Head	Clap

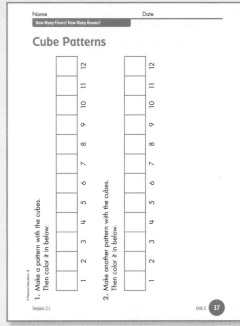

▲ **Student Activity Book, p. 37**

15 MIN INDIVIDUALS

ACTIVITY

2 Make a Repeating Pattern

Students work on making their own repeating patterns and record them on *Student Activity Book* page 37. As you watch students work, remind them that a repeating pattern has a part that repeats over and over. You might ask students to break their cube trains into units to help them identify the part that repeats.

As you watch students work, ask them questions such as the following:

Tell me about your pattern. How does it go? How are your two patterns the same or different? How is your pattern like the one [Holly] made? How is it different?

ONGOING ASSESSMENT: Observing Students at Work

Students make repeating patterns with cubes.

- **Can students make repeating patterns with the cubes?** Do they make 2-element (AB) patterns? Do they use other units that repeat, such as ABC or AABB?

- **How do students describe their patterns to you?** Can they identify the part that repeats?

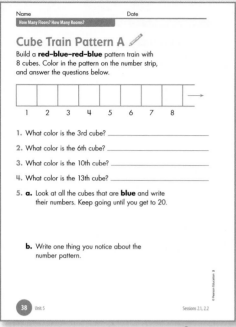

Name _____ Date _____

How Many Floors? How Many Rooms?

Cube Train Pattern A

Build a **red–blue–red–blue** pattern train with 8 cubes. Color in the pattern on the number strip, and answer the questions below.

| | | | | | | | | →

1   2   3   4   5   6   7   8

1. What color is the 3rd cube? _____

2. What color is the 6th cube? _____

3. What color is the 10th cube? _____

4. What color is the 13th cube? _____

5. **a.** Look at all the cubes that are **blue** and write their numbers. Keep going until you get to 20.

    b. Write one thing you notice about the number pattern.

38 Unit 5   Sessions 2.1, 2.2

▲ **Student Activity Book, p. 38** WRITING

DIFFERENTIATION: Supporting the Range of Learners

Intervention If you have students who have not had previous experience with repeating patterns and are not able to make repeating patterns easily, you may want to have them work on some of the activities from the Grade 1 unit, *Color, Shape, and Number Patterns*. In particular, the activities Make a Train and Break a Train focus on how a repeating pattern is constructed from a unit that repeats over and over.

ACTIVITY

3 Introducing the Number Strip

25 MIN   PAIRS   CLASS

Introduce the number strip that students use throughout this Investigation, using the blank number strip and the 2-color cube train from the first part of the session.

This is what we're going to call a number strip. We can use it to record the patterns we make with cubes. We're going to use it to record our red–blue cube train.

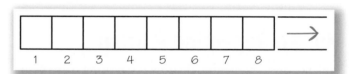

I'm going to color the first square red because the first cube is red. What color goes in the second square? In the third square?

Continue, with you or a student coloring in the squares, until the eight squares are colored in.

I'm going to ask you to think about this pattern. Imagine that it goes on forever and ever in the same way. Close your eyes and picture it in your head. Can you see the pattern going on for a long time? Open your eyes again, and we're going to think about that pattern you imagined in your head. What color is the 10th cube? How do you know?

Keep in mind that there will be a longer discussion of these questions in Session 2.2. Encourage students to keep thinking about these ideas.

Students now work on *Student Activity Book* page 38. Each student works with a partner first to build a cube train, then color in the number strip, and answer the questions. Students should record answers on their own pages. There will be some time for them to continue working on the page in the next session.

ONGOING ASSESSMENT: Observing Students at Work

Students construct an AB pattern with cubes and determine what colors are associated with particular numbers on the number strip.

- **Can students build their trains and color the number strip alternating red, blue, red, blue?**

- **Do students determine the color of cubes associated with given numbers by building the cube pattern, by counting on by 1s, or by reasoning about the numbers (e.g., noticing that the "counting by 2" or even numbers, are always blue)?**

- **Can students describe in some way the numbers associated with the blue cubes?**

DIFFERENTIATION: Supporting the Range of Learners

Intervention Students who cannot visualize how the red–blue pattern continues can extend the pattern with cubes. If students have difficulty coordinating the counting sequence with the pattern, find a way that they can both extend the pattern and write out the numbers. For example, you can cut up a blank 100 chart into strips. Tape two strips together to get 20 squares. Students can number the strips up to 20 and either color the squares lightly—so the numbers still show—or put the cubes along their number strips.

Sample Student Work

SESSION FOLLOW-UP

4 Daily Practice

Daily Practice: For reinforcement of this unit's content, have students complete *Student Activity Book* page 39.

Student Math Handbook: Students and families may use *Student Math Handbook* pages 101, 102, 103 for reference and review. See pages 130–133 in the back of this unit.

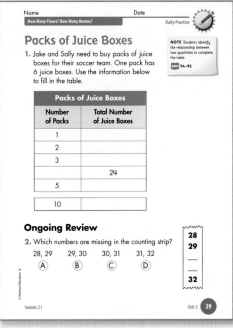

Name _____ Date _____

How Many Floors? How Many Rooms? _____ Daily Practice

Packs of Juice Boxes

NOTE Students identify the relationship between two quantities to complete the table.
SMH 94–95

1. Jake and Sally need to buy packs of juice boxes for their soccer team. One pack has 6 juice boxes. Use the information below to fill in the table.

Packs of Juice Boxes	
Number of Packs	Total Number of Juice Boxes
1	
2	
3	
	24
5	
10	

Ongoing Review

2. Which numbers are missing in the counting strip?

28, 29 29, 30 30, 31 31, 32
(A)   (B)   (C)   (D)

| 28 |
| 29 |
| — |
| — |
| 32 |

Session 2.1   Unit 5 39

▲ **Student Activity Book, p. 39**

Counting by 2s

Math Focus Points

◆ Defining even and odd numbers

◆ Determining and describing the number sequence associated with one of the elements in an AB repeating pattern

◆ Determining the element of a repeating pattern associated with a particular counting number in AB and ABC patterns

Vocabulary

even

odd

Today's Plan		Materials
DISCUSSION **❶ Counting by 2s: Even and Odd Numbers**	20 MIN · CLASS	• *Student Activity Book,* p. 38 (from Session 2.1) • Connecting cubes (as needed); chart paper
ACTIVITY **❷ A 3-Element Pattern**	40 MIN · PAIRS	• *Student Activity Book,* pp. 40–41 • Connecting cubes (yellows, reds, and blues from class set); yellow, red, and blue markers or crayons; pocket 100 chart numbers (optional)
SESSION FOLLOW-UP **❸ Daily Practice and Homework**		• *Student Activity Book,* pp. 42–43 • *Student Math Handbook,* pp. 37, 41–42, 103

Classroom Routines

Quick Images: Coins Using overhead coins, display five dimes and five pennies. Follow the basic *Quick Images* activity. Ask students to focus on the type and number of coins they see as well as the value of the coins. When the coins are covered, ask students to explain how they determined how much money was displayed. Use equations to represent the problem and how students found the total. For example: 10¢ + 10¢ + 10¢ + 10¢ + 10¢ + 5¢ = 55¢ or 10 + 10 + 10 + 10 + 10 = 50 and 50 + 5 = 55. Repeat with six dimes and six pennies.

DISCUSSION

Counting by 2s: Even and Odd Numbers

Math Focus Points for Discussion

◆ Defining even and odd numbers

◆ Determining and describing the number sequence associated with one of the elements in an AB repeating pattern

◆ Determining the element of a repeating pattern associated with a particular counting number in AB patterns

If students need a few minutes to finish *Student Activity Book* page 38, give them some time to do so. Students who are finished should pair up with someone other than their partner in the previous session to compare their work on the page.

Begin the discussion by asking students to share the numbers they wrote for the first ten blue cubes on *Student Activity Book* page 38. Talk about the lists, and help the class resolve any differences in the number sequences students have written. Then write the list of numbers on chart paper, so it can remain posted.

> ## Which Cubes Are Blue Cubes?
> ## 2 4 6 8 10 12 14 16 18 20

Direct students' attention to the list.

What do you notice about the list of numbers?

Some students might notice that the numbers are the "counting by 2" numbers. (You can use the phrase "multiples of 2" to describe this set of numbers, but allow the students to use their own language.) Students are also likely to point out that the numbers on the list are the even numbers, since they defined even numbers in *Stickers, Number Strings, and Story Problems.* If not, review the term *even* numbers with the class. Others might point out that every other number is on the list or that

Professional Development

❶ **Dialogue Box:** "The Reds Are Uneven," p. 126

you add two to get the next number. Encourage students to illustrate their ideas with their cube trains or the colored number strip. Follow up with questions like these:

What would the number for the next blue cube be? How do you know? What about the next one?

Now ask about the numbers for the red squares on the number strip. With the class, make a list of the numbers (in order) associated with the red squares: 1, 3, 5, 7, and so on. Ask students about this list.

What do you notice about the numbers that go below the red squares on your number strip? What would the number for the next red square be? What about the next one? How do you know?

Students will probably volunteer that these are the *odd numbers.* They might notice that this list also has every other number but starts with one instead of two. Second graders often try to figure out what you are "counting by" when you make the list of odd numbers and are surprised to realize that you are counting by two even though it is not the more familiar list that they think of when they think of counting by two.

Finally, choose some numbers later in the pattern, numbers for which students have not yet identified the color of the associated square. Ask students what color the square would be.

Suppose that we kept this same pattern going on the number strip. When I got to 25, what color would the square be? How are you figuring that out? What about for 30—what color would that square be? How do you know?

Students can use cubes or their number strips to figure this out.

In the course of this discussion, as students refer to even or odd numbers, ask them what they mean by *even* and *odd.* They developed definitions in *Stickers, Number Strings, and Story Problems.* This is a good place to review the ideas they came up with then. There are two useful definitions for an even number:

- A number that can be divided into two equal groups of whole things

- A number that can be divided into groups of two without any leftovers

Second graders come up with both of these definitions. On the chart paper, write the definitions your students generate, as a reference for the class.❶

ACTIVITY

② A 3-Element Pattern

40 MIN   **PAIRS**

Introduce this activity with a 3-element body movement pattern, such as clap–slap knees–touch head. Start the pattern, and have students join in as they catch on. Ask students what they can say about the pattern. Sometimes students call this a 1–2–3 pattern or an A–B–C pattern. Use whatever language students bring up to describe the pattern. Then ask,

Who can think of a cube train that matches this clapping pattern? How does it match? Let's try it.

Students match body movements in repeating patterns to cube patterns with the same ABC structure.

Try the body movement pattern again, while saying "red, green, blue" (or whatever colors students suggest). Then introduce *Student Activity Book* pages 40–41.

Today you're going to work on a cube pattern similar to the one that we just did. The new pattern has three colors.

Name _____ Date _____

How Many Floors? How Many Rooms?

Cube Train Pattern B (page 1 of 2)

Build a **yellow–red–blue** pattern train with 9 cubes. Color in the pattern on the number strip, and answer the questions below.

| | | | | | | | | | →
|---|---|---|---|---|---|---|---|---|
| 1 | 2 | 3 | 4 | 5 | 6 | 7 | 8 | 9 |

1. What color is the 3rd cube? _____
2. What color is the 6th cube? _____
3. What color is the 10th cube? _____
4. What color is the 12th cube? _____
5. **a.** Look at all the cubes that are **blue** and write their numbers. Keep going until you get to 30.

   b. Write one thing you notice about the number pattern.

40   Unit 5   Sessions 2.2, 2.3

© Pearson Education 2

▲ **Student Activity Book, p. 40**   PORTFOLIO   WRITING »

Name _____ Date _____

How Many Floors? How Many Rooms?

Cube Train Pattern B (page 2 of 2)

6. **a.** Look at all the cubes that are **yellow** and write their numbers. Keep going until you get past 30.

   b. Write one thing you notice about the number pattern. How is it different from or similar to the list for the **blue** cubes?

7. **a.** Look at all the cubes that are **red** and write their numbers. Keep going until you get past 30.

   b. Write one thing you notice about the number pattern. How is it different from or similar to the list for the **blue** cubes?

© Pearson Education 3

Sessions 2.2, 2.3   Unit 5   41

▲ **Student Activity Book, p. 41**   PORTFOLIO   WRITING »

Students work with a partner first to build a yellow–red–blue cube train and then color in the number strip and answer the questions on *Student Activity Book* pages 40–41. Students should record answers on their own pages.

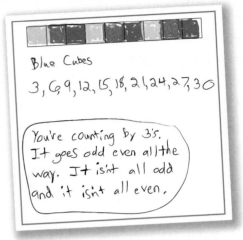

Blue Cubes
3, 6, 9, 12, 15, 18, 21, 24, 27, 30

You're counting by 3's.
It goes odd even all the
way. It isn't all odd
and it isn't all even.

Sample Student Work

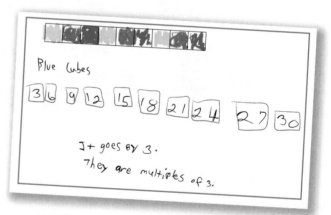

Blue Cubes
3 6 9 12 15 18 21 24 27 30

It goes by 3.
They are multiples of 3.

Sample Student Work

Student Activity Book page 40 is similar to what students did with the AB pattern, red–blue, on *Student Activity Book* page 38. This page focuses on the number pattern associated with the blue cubes (3, 6, 9, 12, . . .). On *Student Activity Book* page 41, students record the number patterns for the yellow cubes (1, 4, 7, 10, . . .) and the red cubes (2, 5, 8, 11, . . .).

Some students might notice during their work today, or in the discussion at the beginning of the next session, that the numbers associated with the blue cubes in the number strip (3, 6, 9, and so on) match the numbers in the second columns of the "Building A" chart and the "Hexagon and Rhombus" table from Investigation 1, which are still posted in the classroom. If students comment on this connection, ask them why they think the tables have the same number sequence. Students can think about this comparison as they continue their work in the next two sessions.

ONGOING ASSESSMENT: Observing Students at Work

Students construct an ABC pattern with the cubes and determine what colors are associated with particular numbers on the number strip.

- **Can students build their trains and color the number strip, alternating yellow, red, blue, yellow, red, blue?**

- **Do students determine the color of cubes associated with given numbers by building the cube pattern, by counting on by 1s, or by reasoning about the pattern of the numbers (e.g., noticing that you count on three to determine the next blue square)?**

- **Can students describe in some way the numbers associated with the blue cubes?** Do they notice that they are counting by 3s?

- **Do students notice that the numbers associated with the blue cubes also appear in the "Building A" chart and the "Hexagon and Rhombus" table?**

DIFFERENTIATION: Supporting the Range of Learners

Intervention As in Session 2.1, some students may need to extend their cube train to 30 and number each cube in the train. They can use the individual numbers from the pocket 100 chart. Questioning students who are reluctant to predict what color a certain cube will be can help them to develop ideas about how to determine it. For example, ask a student who has built a yellow–red–blue train with nine cubes to pause and think about what color the 12th cube will be. Then ask the student to add cubes up to 12. Now ask,

Look at your cube train. You have 12 cubes. What color do you think the 15th cube will be? Just look at it and try to imagine what will happen if you keep building it to 15.

ELL As they extend number patterns in this activity and upcoming sessions, English Language Learners may need to review the words for the counting sequence. You may also wish to work with students on the "counting by" sequences for 2s, 3s, 4s, and 5s as they encounter these in the activities.

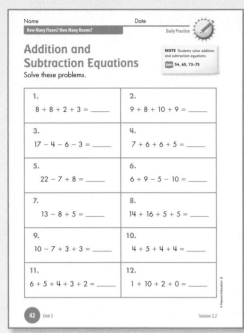

Student Activity Book, p. 42

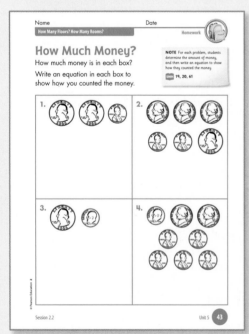

Student Activity Book, p. 43

3 Daily Practice and Homework

 Daily Practice: For ongoing review, have students complete *Student Activity Book* page 42.

 Homework: On *Student Activity Book* page 43, students determine how much money several sets of coins are worth. Then students write an equation for each group of coins to record how they counted the money.

 Student Math Handbook: Students and families may use *Student Math Handbook* pages 37, 41–42, 103 for reference and review. See pages 130–133 in the back of this unit.

Counting by 3s

Math Focus Points

◆ Determining and describing the number sequence associated with one of the elements in an ABC repeating pattern (3, 6, 9, . . . ; 1, 4, 7, . . . ; 2, 5, 8, . . .)

◆ Determining the element of a repeating pattern associated with a particular counting number in ABC and AABBC patterns

◆ Determining how and why the same number sequence can be generated by different contexts

Today's Plan		Materials
① DISCUSSION **Counting by 3s**	25 MIN PAIRS CLASS	• *Student Activity Book,* pp. 40–41 • Chart paper; number strip*; connecting cubes; "Blue Squares" table*
② ACTIVITY **A 5-Element Pattern**	35 MIN PAIRS	• *Student Activity Book,* p. 45 • Connecting cubes; yellow, green, and orange markers or crayons
③ SESSION FOLLOW-UP **Daily Practice**		• *Student Activity Book,* p. 46 • *Student Math Handbook,* p. 103

*See *Materials to Prepare,* p. 75.

Classroom Routines

Today's Number: 32 Using Coins Students individually generate expressions for the number 32 using pennies, nickels, dimes, and quarters. They record these expressions on blank paper, which they have labeled with the date and heading *Today's Number: 32 Using Coins.* This work gives you some information on how students are understanding and working with *Today's Number.* In addition, this is the fifth in a series of work samples for *Today's Number* that will be collected throughout the year.

DISCUSSION

1 Counting by 3s

25 MIN   PAIRS   CLASS

Math Focus Points for Discussion

◆ Determining and describing the number sequence associated with one of the elements in an ABC repeating pattern (3, 6, 9, . . .; 1, 4, 7, . . .; 2, 5, 8, . . .)

◆ Determining the element of a repeating pattern associated with a particular counting number in ABC patterns

◆ Determining how and why the same number sequence can be generated by different contexts

At the start of the session, give students five minutes to compare their work on *Student Activity Book* pages 40–41, the yellow–red–blue pattern, with a student they did not work with in Session 2.2. Then begin the discussion.

This discussion has a structure very similar to the discussion of the red–blue pattern you had in the last session. Draw students' attention to the colored-in yellow–red–blue pattern you have prepared on a number strip.

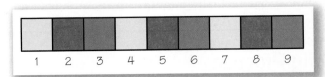

Begin the discussion by asking students to share the numbers they wrote for the first ten blue cubes. Write the list of numbers (3, 6, 9, and so on) on the board or chart paper. Talk about the lists that students wrote, and help the class resolve any differences that students may have in the number sequences.

What do you notice about the numbers in the list?

Some students might notice that they are the "counting by 3" numbers. (You can use the phrase "multiples of 3" to describe this set of numbers, but allow the students to use their own language.) Other students might describe determining the next number in the list by "skipping two numbers" (e.g., skip 1 and 2, say 3, skip 4 and 5, say 6, skip 7 and 8) or by adding three each time. Encourage students to illustrate their ideas with cube trains or on colored number strips. Follow up with questions like these:

What would the number for the next blue cube be? How do you know? What about the next one? If we continued the number strip with this pattern, is there a number that you are sure would be below a blue square? Some of you said this pattern is counting by 3s. Why are you counting by 3s and not counting by 2s? ❶

Now show students the "Blue Squares" table. Ask them to help you fill in the rest of the table. Use your drawing of the yellow–red–blue number strip to show what you mean by "1st blue square," "2nd blue square," and so on.

Blue Squares	Place on Number Strip
	1 2 3 4 5 6 7 8 9
1st blue square	3
2nd blue square	
3rd blue square	
4th blue square	
5th blue square	
6th blue square	
10th blue square	

Ask students how they figured out the number for the 10th blue cube. Then ask students to look around at the other tables you left posted from Investigation 1.

Do you see any of our other tables that look anything like this one? What do you notice? Why do you think these tables have the same list of numbers—3, 6, 9, 12—as the one we just made for the yellow–red–blue pattern?

Students may bring up the "Building A" chart and the "Hexagon and Rhombus" table, which both show a 1:3 relationship. Ask students to remember and describe the situations that generated these tables. Ask,

Do those situations have anything in common with the yellow–red–blue pattern?

Now ask about the numbers for the yellow squares on the number strip. With the class, make a list, in order, of the numbers associated with the yellow cubes: 1, 4, 7, 10, and so on. Ask students about this list.

What do you notice about the numbers that go below the yellow squares on your number strip? What would the next yellow square be? What about the one after that? How do you know?

Professional Development

❶ **Dialogue Box:** Counting by 3s, p. 128

Students might notice that numbers in the list for the yellow squares (except for 1) are one more than the numbers in the list for the blue squares. Other students might notice that, as on the list for blue squares, you can determine the next number on this list by "skipping two numbers." Second graders often try to figure out what you are "counting by" when you make this list of numbers. They notice that you are counting by 3s (or adding on three), even though these numbers are not the multiples of three.

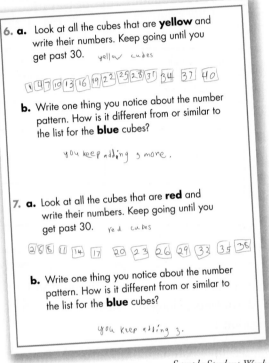

6. **a.** Look at all the cubes that are **yellow** and write their numbers. Keep going until you get past 30. yellow cubes

1 4 7 10 13 16 19 22 25 28 31 34 37 40

b. Write one thing you notice about the number pattern. How is it different from or similar to the list for the **blue** cubes?

you keep adding 3 more.

7. **a.** Look at all the cubes that are **red** and write their numbers. Keep going until you get past 30. red cubes

2 5 8 11 14 17 20 23 26 29 32 35 38

b. Write one thing you notice about the number pattern. How is it different from or similar to the list for the **blue** cubes?

you keep adding 3.

Sample Student Work

ACTIVITY

35 MIN   PAIRS

2 A 5-Element Pattern

Students need to have cubes available as you introduce the 5-element pattern to the class.

Start by having students do the following movement pattern with you: clap–clap–slap knees–slap knees–tap shoulder.

Can you make a cube train that matches this body movement pattern?

Give students just a couple of minutes to make a pattern. Then ask students to share their color patterns and talk about how these patterns match the body movement pattern. Use one of the students' trains to make sure that students know how to continue the pattern until it has at least ten cubes (e.g., red–red–blue–blue–yellow–red–red–blue–blue–yellow). Ask students to identify the unit of the pattern.

What is the part of our body movement pattern that repeats over and over? What is the part of our cube pattern that repeats over and over? Take a close look. Where does it start over again?

Students now work on *Student Activity Book* page 45. Although students may work in pairs, each student should complete his or her own page. Note that as the repeating patterns become less familiar—like this one— more students may need to extend the pattern with cubes. However, students have worked on counting by 5s, and they do have experience with this number sequence. Once they notice that the number sequence for the orange cubes is the multiples of five, they may be able to extend it without building their cube trains all the way to 50.

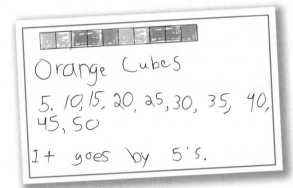

Sample Student Work

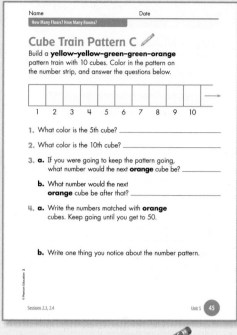

▲ Student Activity Book, p. 45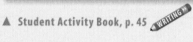

✔ ONGOING ASSESSMENT: Observing Students at Work

Students construct an AABBC pattern with cubes and determine what colors are associated with particular numbers on the number strip.

- **Can students build their trains and color the number strip?** Do they see the "fiveness" of the pattern, even though there are only three colors?

- **Do students determine the color of cubes associated with given numbers by building the cube pattern, by counting on by 1s, or by reasoning about the pattern of the numbers (e.g., noticing that you count on five to determine the next orange square)?**

- **Can students describe in some way the numbers associated with the orange cubes?** Do they notice they are counting by 5s?

- **Do students notice that the numbers associated with the orange cubes also appear in the "Building B" chart?**

Name Date

How Many Floors? How Many Rooms? Daily Practice

Tricycle Wheels

NOTE Students identify the relationship between two quantities to complete the table. SMH 94–95

1. Franco and Kira are decorating tricycle wheels for their neighborhood parade. Fill in the table to find how many wheels they need to decorate if there are 15 tricycles.

Tricycle Wheels	
Number of Tricycles	**Total Number of Wheels**
1	3
2	
3	
4	
5	
10	
11	
12	
15	

Ongoing Review

2. Which shows a combination of 12?

6 + 9 Ⓐ 7 + 5 Ⓑ 3 + 8 Ⓒ 5 + 5 Ⓓ

46 Unit 5 Session 2.3

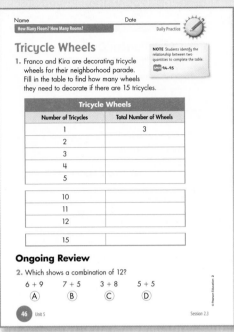

▲ Student Activity Book, p. 46

DIFFERENTIATION: Supporting the Range of Learners

Intervention Students who are not easily generating the number sequences that go with a particular color can benefit from working on another ABC pattern instead of going on to this AABBC pattern. For example, ask students to make a green–yellow–orange pattern with 12 cubes. Pose a few questions such as, *What are the numbers that go with all the orange cubes? What color will the 15th cube be? What color will the 16th cube be?* Or, students can work on the AABBC pattern, building it and then writing down the number sequence up to 20 rather than to 50.

3 SESSION FOLLOW-UP
Daily Practice

Daily Practice: For reinforcement of this unit's content, have students complete *Student Activity Book* page 46.

Student Math Handbook: Students and families may use Student Math Handbook page 103 for reference and review. See pages 130–133 in the back of this unit.

How Is Red–Blue–Brown–Green Like Yellow–Black–White–Orange?

Math Focus Points

- Determining and describing the number sequence associated with one of the elements in an AABBC or ABCD repeating pattern (5, 10, 15, . . . , and 4, 8, 12, . . .)

- Determining the element of a repeating pattern associated with a particular counting number in AABBC or ABCD patterns

- Determining how and why the same number sequence can be generated by different contexts

Vocabulary

multiple

Today's Plan		Materials
DISCUSSION **① Counting by 5s**	10 MIN CLASS	• *Student Activity Book,* p. 45 • Number strip 1*; chart paper (as needed; optional)
ACTIVITY **② Constructing 4-Element Patterns**	35 MIN PAIRS	• *Student Activity Book,* pp. 47–49 • Connecting cubes (as needed)
DISCUSSION **③ How Is Red–Blue–Brown–Green Like Yellow–Black–White–Orange?**	15 MIN CLASS	• *Student Activity Book,* pp. 47–49 • "Green Squares" table*; number strips 2 and 3*
SESSION FOLLOW-UP **④ Daily Practice and Homework**		• *Student Activity Book,* pp. 50–51 • *Student Math Handbook,* pp. 101, 103

*See *Materials to Prepare,* p. 75.

Classroom Routines

What Time Is It? Students work with a partner to practice setting their individual clocks to the quarter hour. They take turns with one student suggesting a time, and the other one setting the time. For some students, working with 45 minutes past the hour may also be appropriate.

DISCUSSION

① Counting by 5s

10 MIN   CLASS

Math Focus Points for Discussion

◈ Determining and describing the number sequence associated with one of the elements in an AABBC repeating pattern (5, 10, 15, . . .)

◈ Determining the element of a repeating pattern associated with a particular counting number in AABBC patterns

◈ Determining how and why the same number sequence can be generated by different contexts

At the start of the session, give students five minutes to get out *Student Activity Book* page 45 (the yellow–yellow–green–green–orange pattern) and compare answers with another student.

Since students have had several of these discussions, keep this one brief, so that they have time to work on the next activity and are ready for the final discussion.

Draw students' attention to the colored-in yellow–yellow–green–green–orange pattern that you have prepared on a number strip.

Students discuss what numbers are associated with the orange squares.

Begin the discussion by asking students to share the numbers they wrote on page 45 for the first ten orange cubes. Write the list of numbers (5, 10, 15, and so on) on the board or chart paper. Talk about the lists and help the class resolve any differences in the number sequences that students have written. Then ask,

What do you notice about the numbers in the list?

Some might notice that they are the "counting by 5" numbers. You can also use the phrase "multiples of 5" to describe this set of numbers, but allow the students to use their own language. Other students might describe determining the next number in the list by "skipping four numbers" (e.g., say 5, skip 6, 7, 8, 9, say 10) or by adding five each time.

Encourage students to illustrate their ideas with their cube trains or on the colored number strip. Follow up with questions like these:

What would the number for the next orange cube be? How do you know? What about the next one? If we continued the number strip with this pattern, is there a number that you are sure would be below an orange square? How do you know?

Also, ask students whether they see this number sequence anywhere in the tables from Investigation 1. Students may notice that the 5, 10, 15, . . . sequence appears in the "Building B" table.

Why do you think the same number sequence works for the orange squares in our pattern and for Building B?

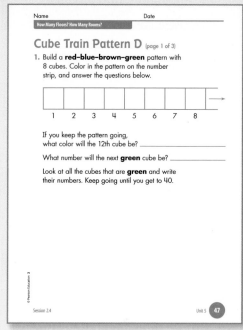

▲ **Student Activity Book, p. 47**

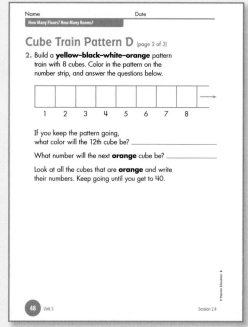

▲ **Student Activity Book, p. 48**

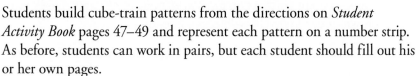

ACTIVITY

2 Constructing 4-Element Patterns

35 MIN   PAIRS

Students build cube-train patterns from the directions on *Student Activity Book* pages 47–49 and represent each pattern on a number strip. As before, students can work in pairs, but each student should fill out his or her own pages.

On *Student Activity Book* pages 47–49, students build two different cube train patterns, each from a 4-element unit: red–blue–brown–green and yellow–black–white–orange. Students identify numbers associated with the last cube in each unit (the multiples of 4) and describe what is the same and what is different about the two patterns.

Finally, students are asked to create another pattern that results in the same number sequence (4, 8, 12, 16, . . .) for one of the colors in this new pattern.

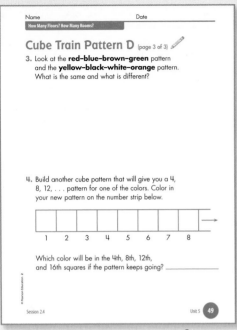

▲ **Student Activity Book, p. 49**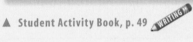

ONGOING ASSESSMENT: Observing Students at Work

Students build repeating patterns with four-element units, and
associate a number sequence with the last cube in each unit.

- **Do students determine the color of cubes associated with given
  numbers by building the cube pattern, by counting on by 1s, or
  by reasoning about the pattern of the numbers (e.g., noticing
  that you count on four to determine the next green square in
  red–blue–brown–green)?**

- **Do students notice that the numbers are the same for the green
  cubes and the orange cubes in the two patterns?** Can they explain
  why this is true?

- **When they build their own cube trains, do students create
  patterns with 4-element units?**

DISCUSSION

3

How Is Red–Blue–Brown–Green Like Yellow–Black–White–Orange?

15 MIN   CLASS

Math Focus Points for Discussion

◆ Determining and describing the number sequence associated with
  one of the elements in an ABCD repeating pattern (4, 8, 12, . . .)

◆ Determining how and why the same number sequence can be
  generated by different contexts

Draw students' attention to the two number strips you have made for the
two 4-element patterns on *Student Activity Book* pages 47–49 red–blue–
brown–green and yellow–black–white–orange.

What is the same and what is different about these two patterns?

Students may note that the colors are different, but there are four colors in each unit.

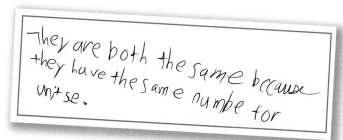

They are both the same because they have the same numbe for unitse.

Sample Student Work

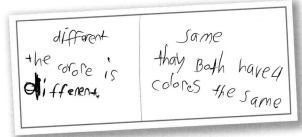

different
the corore is different.

same
thay Both have 4 colores the same

Sample Student Work

Students will probably also bring up the numbers they listed for the green squares in the first pattern and the orange squares in the second pattern. If not, follow up with questions like these:

What did you notice about the numbers on your list for the green cubes and the numbers on your list for the orange cubes? Why are the numbers on the two lists the same? Why are they the multiples of four?

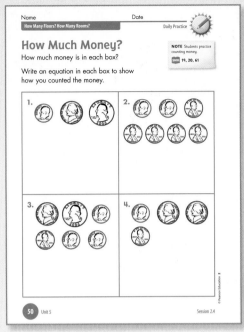

▲ **Student Activity Book, p. 50**

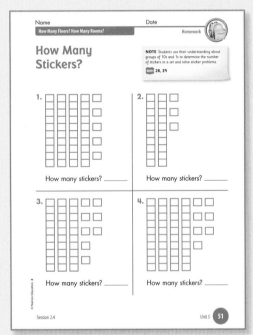

▲ **Student Activity Book, p. 51**

Show students the table you started for the green square in the red–blue–brown–green pattern.

Green Squares	Place on Number Strip
	1 2 3 4 5 6 7 8
1st green square	4
2nd green square	
3rd green square	
4th green square	
5th green square	
6th green square	
10th green square	

Ask students to help you complete the table. Then ask,

Do you see any of our other tables with a pattern like this one? What do you notice? Why do you think these tables have the same list of numbers—4, 8, 12, 16, . . . ?

Students may see that the tables for Buildings C and E—with four rooms per floor—show the same numerical relationship as these four-element patterns. You might also ask students why there is no pattern block poster with this number sequence.

SESSION FOLLOW-UP

4 Daily Practice and Homework

 Daily Practice: For ongoing review, have students complete *Student Activity Book* page 50.

 Homework: On *Student Activity Book* page 51, students use their understanding about groups of 10s and 1s to determine the number of stickers.

Student Math Handbook: Students and families may use *Student Math Handbook* pages 101, 103 for reference and review. See pages 130–133 in the back of this unit.

End-of-Unit Assessment

Math Focus Points

◆ Connecting numbers in a table to the situation they represent

◆ Finding the value of one quantity in a constant ratio situation, given the value of the other

◆ Determining the element of a repeating pattern associated with a particular counting number in an AB or AAB pattern

Today's Plan		Materials
ASSESSMENT ACTIVITY **① End-of-Unit Assessment**	✔ 🕐 👤 **60 MIN** **INDIVIDUALS**	• M14–M17*
SESSION FOLLOW-UP **② Daily Practice**		• *Student Activity Book,* p. 53 • *Student Math Handbook,* pp. 96, 97–98 100, 103

*See *Materials to Prepare,* p. 75.

Classroom Routines

Quick Images: Pattern Blocks Using *Quick Images with Pattern Blocks 1* (T49–T50), display Image 1. Follow the basic *Quick Images* activity. Ask students to determine the total number of trapezoids and share their strategies. Repeat with Image 2 and then Image 3.

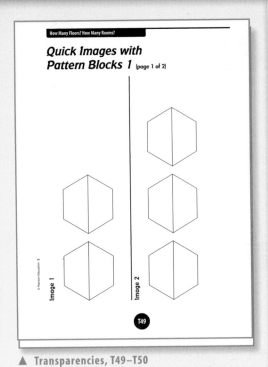

How Many Floors? How Many Rooms?

Quick Images with
Pattern Blocks 1 (page 1 of 2)

Image 1

Image 2

T49

▲ **Transparencies, T49–T50**

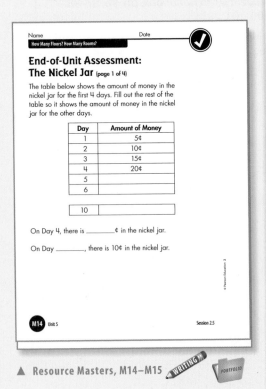

Name _____ Date _____

How Many Floors? How Many Rooms?

End-of-Unit Assessment:
The Nickel Jar (page 1 of 4)

The table below shows the amount of money in the
nickel jar for the first 4 days. Fill out the rest of the
table so it shows the amount of money in the nickel
jar for the other days.

Day	Amount of Money
1	5¢
2	10¢
3	15¢
4	20¢
5	
6	
10	

On Day 4, there is _____ ¢ in the nickel jar.

On Day _____, there is 10¢ in the nickel jar.

M14 Unit 5   Session 2.5

▲ **Resource Masters, M14–M15** WRITING PORTFOLIO

ASSESSMENT ACTIVITY

1 End-of-Unit Assessment

60 MIN INDIVIDUALS

Let students know that today they are going to work individually on
some problems about patterns. Each of the two End-of-Unit Assessment
problems, The Nickel Jar (M14–M15) and Shape Patterns (M16–M17),
is related to the work students have done in the unit, although the
contexts are different. Students can work on the problems in any order.

In The Nickel Jar problems (M14–M15), students complete, describe,
and use information from a table that represents a ratio relationship
in a new context. This problem set addresses Benchmark 1: Explain what
the numbers in a table represent in a constant ratio situation (involving
ratios of 1:2, 1:3, 1:4, 1:5, and 1:6); and Benchmark 2: Complete and
extend a table to match a situation involving a constant ratio.

In the second set of problems, Shape Patterns (M16–M17), students
complete two repeating shape patterns and consider where the shapes
will fall if the pattern continues. These problems address Benchmark 3:
Extend a repeating pattern and determine what element of the pattern
will be in a particular position (e.g., the 16th position) if the pattern
keeps going.

Make sure that students understand the directions for each assessment.
One way to proceed is to have all students start with The Nickel Jar
(M14–M15), so that you can explain the directions to everyone. Students
who had the Grade 1 unit, *Color, Shape, and Number Patterns,* last year
are familiar with the Penny Jar context. Draw a picture of a jar on the
board so that students can visualize the context. Make sure that students
understand the idea of a jar used to save money and that the same
amount of money is put in each day. In helping students understand
the context, avoid talking about five cents directly. Part of what is being
assessed is whether students can get this information from the table.

As students finish, they can go on to work on Shape Patterns (M16–M17).
This work with a repeating pattern should be familiar. Make sure that
students can read the questions. Note that it is critical for students to
respond to the questions about their reasoning (e.g., How did you figure
out the 12th shape?). Since there are only two possible responses to
the shape questions (circle or square; moon or star), students can often
get a correct answer even if they do not extend the pattern correctly.
Therefore, make sure that students are writing enough for you to
understand their thinking. If some students cannot record their methods
themselves, have them tell you how they approached the problems, and
record what they say on their papers so that you have a record of it.❶

Do as much observation and note-taking as you can as students engage in the assessment. The assessment pages will provide some information, but you will gain more information through observing students' work.❷

If you have some time at the end of the session after students have finished, choose one of the problems to talk about in a class discussion.

DIFFERENTIATION: Supporting the Range of Learners

ELL It may be helpful to model the Nickel Jar problem for English Language Learners using an actual jar and nickels to help them understand this problem's context. Some students may not be able to fully express in writing their response to the final question, *How did you figure out how much money is in the nickel jar on the 10th day?* In this case, they can first explain their ideas to you verbally, and then you can help them put their ideas into writing.

SESSION FOLLOW-UP
❷ Daily Practice

 Daily Practice: For enrichment, have students complete *Student Activity Book* page 53.

 Student Math Handbook: Students and families may use *Student Math Handbook* pages 96, 97–98, 100, 103 for reference and review. See pages 130–133 in the back of this unit.

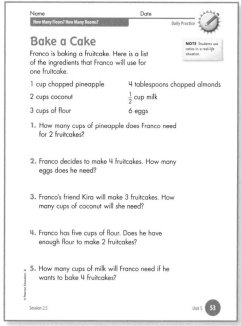

▲ **Student Activity Book, p. 53**

Teaching Note

❶ **Student Support** Make sure that all students have whatever support they need to understand the format and directions of the assessment so that you get a fair reading of the students' performance on the mathematics problems.

Professional Development

❷ **Teacher Note:** End-of-Unit Assessment, p. 114

▲ **Resource Masters, M16–M17**

In Part 6 of *Implementing Investigations in Grade 2*, you will find a set of Teacher Notes that addresses topics and issues applicable to the curriculum as a whole rather than to specific curriculum units. They include the following:

Computational Fluency and Place Value

Computational Algorithms and Methods

Representations and Contexts for Mathematical Work

Foundations of Algebra in the Elementary Grades

Discussing Mathematical Ideas

Racial and Linguistic Diversity in the Classroom:
   What Does Equity Mean in Today's Math Classroom?

Equal Groups and Ratio

In Grade 2, students are beginning to think about counting by groups. Although they are not formally using multiplication notation, they are beginning to build a foundation of knowledge about equal groups. This unit helps them become more familiar with the idea of equal groups. They encounter some of the "counting by" patterns they are coming to know—counting by 2s and by 5s—and they learn less familiar counting sequences, such as counting by 3s, 4s, and 6s.

In this unit, students build and model ratio situations that involve accumulating equal groups. In a situation with a constant ratio, one variable changes by a constant amount in relation to another variable that also changes by a constant amount. For example, as students make buildings out of connecting cubes, they might add on three cubes for each "floor" of the building. The number of cubes increases by three each time—3, 6, 9, 12, and so on—as the number of "floors" increases by one. When they work with pattern blocks, students notice, for example, that it takes two trapezoid pattern blocks to cover each of the hexagons. Each time one more hexagon is covered, the number of trapezoids increases by two.

These contexts give students many opportunities to add on or count by equal groups. In Session 1.1, students discuss how to find the number of rooms in five floors of Building A (*Student Activity Book* page 3), which has three rooms per floor, and then use this information to find the number of rooms in ten floors. During this discussion, you can begin to see the range of ways in which your students think about equal groups.

Some students use the equal number of rooms per floor to find the total. They add on or count by that number. They might say, "3 plus 3 is 6, and then 3 is 9, and then another 3—10, 11, 12—and then 13, 14, 15." Many students use a strategy like this one, adding for combinations they know, such as 3 + 3, and counting on for less familiar combinations, such as 12 + 3. Some students build on the combinations they know (e.g., "3 plus 3 is 6, and then

there's another 3 plus 3 is 6, so that's 6 plus 6 is 12, and then another 3—13, 14, 15").

Because students are more familiar with counting by 5s than with counting by 3s, some students notice that they can count by the columns of the building, rather than by the layers. Since there are five floors, they count each stack of rooms—5, 10, 15—often running their fingers up the columns to show the 5s.

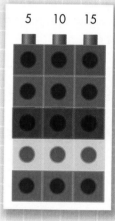

Counting by the number of cubes in each column is another effective method of using equal groups to help find the total in the cube-building context. However, in the pattern block context (Sessions 1.5 and 1.6), there is not a comparable alternate way of counting.

Many students count by 1s but use the equal groupings to help them keep track. For example, one student said, "If you count around the top five times, you get to 15." She counted by 1s, but grouped the 1s by 3s, with a pause in between: 1, 2, 3, . . . 4, 5, 6, . . . 7, 8, 9, . . .10, 11, 12, . . . 13, 14, 15. However, some students will not yet see that noticing equal groups can help them count the total number of cubes. They count by ones without making use of the structure of equal groups. As the unit continues, help these students begin to notice equal groups by encouraging them to combine at least two groups before they count on the rest by 1s.

Keep in mind that counting by 3s, 4s, or 6s is not familiar for most second graders. It is not expected that they will be fluent with counting by these numbers by the end of this unit, but they will gain more experience with combinations of 3s, 4s, and 6s. Encourage students to use what they know, such as the doubles 3 + 3 and 4 + 4, and to build on those to make further combinations. For more about how students use doubling to help them find the total number of rooms for ten floors of a cube building, see the **Teacher Note:** Using a Doubling Strategy to Reason About Ratios, page 109.

In Investigation 2, students continue to study multiples of 2, 3, 4, and 5 as they build repeating color patterns on a number strip like this one.

For example, as this repeating pattern continues, the number sequence that goes with the green squares is

3, 6, 9, 12, 15, 18, 21, 24, 27, 30, . . .

The unit of this pattern is three squares long (red, blue, green). This unit is repeated over and over, so the pattern is formed by groups of three. The last square in each unit is numbered by a multiple of three.

As students figure out why the series 3, 6, 9, 12, . . . goes with the green squares, they notice how they start with three and then count on or add on three more each time. As one student said about a yellow–red–orange repeating cube pattern, "I think it's three because the orange is at the end. So, you have to count the first one, and that would be a yellow, and the second one is a red. Then we get to orange if we count one more." See **Dialogue Box: Counting by 3s**, page 128.

Using and Interpreting Tables

A table is a useful representation of the relationship between two quantities. In this unit, second graders learn about and use tables to record the relationships they see as they build with connecting cubes or pattern blocks.

In Session 1.1, students begin with the problem of finding the total number of rooms in a building with ten floors and three rooms per floor. As they make their own representations of their solutions, they become aware of the relationship between the two quantities—that an increase of one in the total number of floors is related to an increase of three in the total number of rooms.

After working through this problem, students are introduced to tables in Session 1.2. As adults, we have seen tables often and have some sense of how they structure information. However, a table full of vertical and horizontal lines, words, and numbers does not necessarily make sense at first to a second grader. Only through moving back and forth between the numbers in the table and the situation they represent do students begin to develop an understanding of what information is provided and how the parts of the table are related.

One of the key issues in learning about tables is understanding what the information in each column and row means.

Total Number of Floors	Total Number of Rooms
1	3
2	6
3	9
4	12
5	15

By looking at each column, we can see how each of the quantities changes. The first column of this table shows that the number of floors is increasing by one; the second column shows that the total number of rooms increases by three as each floor is added. Students in the elementary grades often find the number patterns they see in a column of a table compelling. If students see a column in which the numbers are 3, 6, 9, it is easy for them to simply continue the pattern they see—counting by or adding on 3s—without having a sense of what those numbers mean. Ask students to show you what the numbers mean on the cube building itself.

It is also crucial to help students focus on the numbers in each row of the table because it is the row that shows the relationship *between* the two quantities and the underlying constant ratio. Continually making connections between what the students are building and the numbers in the table helps students bring meaning to the interpretation of a table. The individual assessment that you carry out with each student in Sessions 1.4, 1.5, and 1.6 is focused on students' understanding about what the numbers in each row of a table mean. For example, a student who says, "For 4 floors there are 12 rooms because there are 3 rooms for every floor, so 3 + 3 + 3 + 3 makes 12" is describing how the numbers 4 and 12 in the table make sense in terms of the cube building context. If a student says, "It's 12 because it goes 3, 6, 9, 12," ask the student to show how he or she sees "3, 6, 9, 12" in the cube building.

In talking about tables with your students, it is useful to use the words *row* (to mean a horizontal slice of the table) and *column* (to mean a vertical slice of the table). When you use these words, indicate with gestures what part of the table you are referencing. It is not important for students to learn definitions of these words out of context. However, students can learn their meaning through listening to you and watching you model their correct use. In time, this will help students think through and talk about the structure of the information in a table.

In Session 1.2, students are introduced to a table with a gap. We use this convention to indicate missing rows in the table:

Total Number of Floors	Total Number of Rooms
1	4
2	8
3	12
4	16
5	20
10	

In this table, rows 6, 7, 8, and 9 are missing. Rows are left out to encourage students to think about and describe the relationship of the two quantities, rather than just continue number patterns down the columns. Many students will need to talk through the meaning of these gaps. Students often think that the missing value in this table should be 24; they are adding on another 4 to the previous value in the second column. Remind students to check the number in the first column to give them information about the number of floors (or, in Sessions 1.5 and 1.6, the quantity of a particular pattern block). Students are likely to see tables in which values are arranged in a variety of ways. They can start learning now that the values in a column of a table may not always be sequenced in the way they expect. They need to actually look at what the values are and relate them to the situation they represent.

Teacher Note

Using a Doubling Strategy to Reason About Ratios

As students work with the cube buildings and pattern blocks in Investigation 1, you will see a range of strategies used. Many students count, skip-count, or add on to find the total number of rooms for a certain number of floors or the total number of pattern block shapes used to cover another shape. See **Teacher Note:** Equal Groups and Ratio, page 105.

Some students will use what they know about addition combinations to reason about the total number of rooms or pattern blocks. For example, some students were looking at a cube building with six rooms on each floor.

For 2 floors, Holly said, "I knew it was 12 because I doubled 6 to get 12."

For 4 floors, Nate said, "I doubled 12. It's 24. 12 plus 12 is 24."

For 5 floors, Jacy said, "I saw that when there were 5 floors, it's 2 floors plus 3 floors. So, that's 12 plus 18, and that's 30."

Doubling, in particular, is likely to come up from some of your students. Doubling is a useful strategy that other students can learn in the course of the investigation. However, it is important that students keep thinking about what they are doubling and why. In this classroom example in which the students are thinking about a building with five rooms on a floor, the teacher realizes that students are doubling numbers but have lost track of why it makes sense to do so.

Teacher: We've figured out the number of rooms for 1, 2, 3, 4, and 5 floors. What about 10 floors?

Carolina: 50. Because we double 25.

Teacher: Carolina, why did you double 25?

Carolina: Because you're supposed to double. Because that's how you get the answer. I doubled it because . . . I don't know why I did it!

Teacher: We're on the fifth floor and we had 25 rooms. And now we have ten floors. Who can explain why it makes sense to double the 25?

Gregory: It's like you're adding five more stories to reach the tenth floor.

Juan: You double five and five to get to the tenth floor. And for 25, you have to double. It's almost the same thing.

Rochelle: 25 more rooms, because you double 25, because five rooms are in one story. And you add five, you add five 5s, and that equals 25. You have 25 rooms.

Teacher: Maybe I'll build this building. [The teacher builds the building below.] Now I have five floors and I'm tired of counting so many rooms. How many more rooms will I have if I have ten floors?

Alberto: 25 more.

Tia: You're skipping floors, and you have to add the number of floors you skip.

Malcolm: You need 25 rooms to get to the tenth floor.

Seeing that two buildings are the same often sparks ideas about doubling. For example, in one classroom Melissa was working on a building with 6 rooms per floor. She had constructed the building with 5 floors and found that there were 30 rooms in the building. Then, as she was thinking about how to find the number of rooms in 10 floors, she noticed that Carla, working next to her, had solved the same problem she had just solved, so they both had five-floor buildings with 6 rooms per floor. Melissa put the two buildings together and counted the cubes to get 60 and then exclaimed, "Oh, it's 60. [She records 60 in the table.] Oh, wait, oh, man I can't believe I just did that. I should have known it was 60!" When the teacher asked her what she meant, she said, "Look, it was five plus five is ten, so I just needed to do 30 plus 30 to get 60. Oh, I should have thought of that!"

However, when Melissa worked on another building, she seemed overwhelmed when she reached the row in the table for 10 floors. Only when the teacher referred her back to her previous work did she realize that she could use her doubling idea again. Like most second graders, Melissa will need to continue to ground her numerical reasoning in what is going on in the situation that the numbers represent.

As the unit progresses, some of the tables jump from 6 to 10, not from 5 to 10 (see *Student Activity Book* pages 11–18 in the context of cube buildings). Some students might quickly double the number of rooms for 6 floors to get the number of rooms for 10 floors because that method worked when the table jumped from 5 to 10 floors. These students have lost track of what the numbers mean and why they are doubling. Ask them to explain their method to you in terms of rooms and floors, not just the numbers in the table. Ask, for example, "How many more floors do you need to add to your building to get from 6 floors up to 10 floors? So, if there are 5 rooms on each floor, how many more 5s do you need?"

Students' Difficulties with Mystery Shapes

The Mystery Shapes activity provides partial tables that give some information about a relationship between two pattern block shapes. During most of this investigation, students have been starting with a concrete situation and then completing a table with numbers they derive from that situation. Now students are asked to look at a table and imagine what the concrete situation could be—in this case, what are two pattern blocks that have a relationship that match the numbers in the table?

At first, students work with a table that provides information about a known shape in the first column and an unknown shape in the second column.

Number of Hexagons ⬡	Number of Mystery Shape
1	
2	6
3	9
4	
5	
6	18

Some of these tables do not provide a number for the mystery shape in the first row, so students have to reason from information in a later row. Students may need some help in understanding how to work with the information in a table when they cannot start with the first row, as in this classroom conversation:

Teacher: Look at this row. You need six of the mystery shape to cover two hexagons. What could it be?

Some students: Six triangles.

Other students: Six rhombuses.

Teacher: Let's see what works out.

Students try it and find that they can cover two hexagons with six rhombuses, but several students are showing one hexagon covered by six triangles. Even though the table indicates that six of the mystery shape cover two hexagons, they are used to working with just one shape.

Teacher: So, what do you think? Look at this row of the table—two hexagons covered by six somethings. What do you think?

Rochelle: It takes six triangles for just one hexagon, not for two.

Simon: OK, but I still don't understand what you're talking about.

Chen: It's because in the table, look, it's two hexagons that make six, but if you use triangles then you can't get two because it takes six to fill the whole hexagon.

Simon: Oh, six of something for two hexagons.

With some support in formulating the question, students generally find these first Mystery Shape tables fairly accessible and understand what problem they are trying to solve. However, *Student Activity Book* pages 29–30 present a further complication. On these pages, the first column of the table is the mystery shape, while the shape in the second column—the number of blocks used to cover the first shape—is given.

Number of Mystery Shape	Number of Triangles △
1	
2	12
3	18
4	
5	

In one classroom, a teacher is helping a student who appears to be stuck.

Teacher: What information does the table tell you?

Carla: That's two for 12.

Teacher: 12 what?

Carla: 12 of these [holds up a triangle].

Teacher: OK, so you need 12 of these. [Carla puts out 12 triangles.] Now these have to cover two of the mystery shape.

Carla holds up a hexagon.

Teacher: Are you sure?

Carla: No.

Teacher: Can you test it?

Carla covers two hexagons with the 12 triangles.

Teacher: Did it work out? How will you fill in the rest of the table?

Carla: For one, it's six, and it's going by 6s. So, it's 12 for two, and then six more. [She counts six onto 12.] 18.

Teacher: So, what does that 18 mean?

Carla: It's three hexagons and 18 triangles.

Teacher: Does that work? Why don't you test it out?

In this exchange, the teacher works with the student to interpret the table by helping her state the question. The teacher then asks her to try out her ideas with pattern blocks and relate the numbers in the table to what she constructs with the blocks.

Teacher Note

Repeating Patterns

All of the patterns in Investigation 2 are built by repeating a basic unit. The simplest repeating pattern is constructed by repeating a unit that has two different elements that alternate, such as a border of tiles in a red–yellow–red–yellow sequence around the edge of a bathtub. A repeating pattern with two elements that alternate can be referred to as an AB pattern. In this case, the A designates a red tile and the B designates a yellow tile:

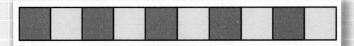

In this tile pattern, the unit consists of a red tile followed by a yellow tile:

A *unit* is the segment of the pattern that is repeated over and over.

In Investigation 2, students study more complicated patterns, including the color patterns red–blue–brown–green and red–red–blue–blue–yellow. A cube "train" made up of the blocks red–red–blue–blue–yellow–red–red–blue–blue–yellow has *red–red–blue–blue–yellow* as its unit. We can call this pattern an AABBC pattern because its unit consists of three elements, the first of which occurs twice (AA), the second of which occurs twice (BB), and the third of which occurs once (C). As the repeating unit of a pattern gets larger and more complex, it may become difficult to identify that unit from looking at the pattern. In an AABBC pattern, the repeating unit may be harder to see.

In Grade 1, students worked with repeating patterns, often answering the question "What comes next?" It is important to note that unless you are told that you have enough

information to analyze the structure of a repeating pattern and identify the unit, it is always possible that the visible part of a sequence is part of a larger pattern and that you do not have enough information to describe it. Some students might bring up that there are other possible ways to extend the beginning of a repeating pattern. You can acknowledge that this is an important idea, but explain that, in these cases, the pattern does continue to repeat in the same way.

In Grade 1, students also began to look at repeating patterns labeled with the counting numbers. In part, the numbering was for convenience and clarity when discussing the pattern. ("What color do you think the eighth cube will be if we continue the pattern?" "Why do you think the 10th cube will be red?") However, some students in Grade 1 also noticed that the number sequences give information about the pattern. In Grade 2, students work with the idea that the number sequence for a certain element in the repeating pattern is related to the length of the repeating unit. For example, in a yellow–orange–red pattern, the number sequence for the red squares is 3, 6, 9, 12, 15, 18, ... The number sequence for the yellow squares is 1, 4, 7, 10, 13, . . . :

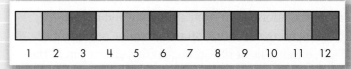

In each number sequence, the numbers are three apart. Because the unit has three elements, each element occurs on every third number, but the sequences for each color begin at different numbers. In particular, the last element in the unit has a number sequence of the multiples of the length of the unit. In this case, the red square is the last element in the repeating unit. The number sequence for the red squares is 3, 6, 9, 12, and so on—the multiples of three. The relationship between these number sequences and ideas about functions is discussed further in **Algebra Connections in This Unit,** page 16.

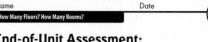

Teacher Note

End-of-Unit Assessment

Problem 1: The Nickel Jar

In End-of-Unit Assessment: The Nickel Jar (M14–M15), students complete a table about a jar in which 5¢ is placed each day. They fill in sentences about two different rows of the table. Then, they determine how much money will be in the nickel jar on the 10th day and the 14th day and explain their solutions.

Benchmarks addressed

Benchmark 1: Explain what the numbers in a table represent in a constant ratio situation (involving ratios of 1:2, 1:3, 1:4, 1:5, and 1:6).

Benchmark 2: Complete and extend a table to match a situation involving a constant ratio.

In order to meet the benchmarks, students' work should show that they can:

• Fill in a partially completed table that represents a constant ratio between two quantities;

• Read and interpret a row of the table;

• Use the information from a situation and a table representing that situation to determine one quantity given the value of the other quantity, after a gap in the sequence (in this problem, finding the amount of money in the jar on Days 10 and 14);

• Provide an explanation of how they figured out these quantities.

Name _____ Date _____

How Many Floors? How Many Rooms?

End-of-Unit Assessment: The Nickel Jar (page 1 of 4)

The table below shows the amount of money in the nickel jar for the first 4 days. Fill out the rest of the table so it shows the amount of money in the nickel jar for the other days.

Day	Amount of Money
1	5¢
2	10¢
3	15¢
4	20¢
5	
6	

10	

On Day 4, there is _____¢ in the nickel jar.

On Day _____, there is 10¢ in the nickel jar.

▲ Resource Masters, M14

Name _____ Date _____

How Many Floors? How Many Rooms?

End-of-Unit Assessment: The Nickel Jar (page 2 of 4)

How did you figure out how much money is in the nickel jar on Day 10?

How much money will be in the nickel jar on Day 14?

_____

Show how you figured this out.

▲ Resource Masters, M15

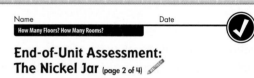

Meeting the Benchmarks

In this problem, the focus is on students' understanding of the meaning of the table and using the ratio relationship between the number of days and amount of money in the jar to figure out how much money is in the jar on the 10th and 14th day.

In students' solutions to this problem, look for the following:

Students who meet the benchmark fill in the table correctly for Day 5 (25¢) and Day 6 (30¢), fill in the sentences at the bottom of page 1 correctly (On Day 4, there is <u>20¢</u> in the nickel jar; on Day <u>2</u>, there is 10¢ in the nickel jar), and determine the amount of money in the jar on Days 10 and 14 (50¢ and 70¢). These students are understanding the relationship between a quantity in the first column—the number of days—and the corresponding quantity in the second column—the total amount of money.

To find the amount of money in the jar on Day 10 and Day 14, many students count up by 5s from 30¢. These students realize that they have to count up 5¢ for each of four more days and find ways to accurately keep track of the number of 5s they need. Here are two examples:

How did you figure out how much money is in the nickel jar on Day 10?

I said to myself becaues you left off from 30, 35, 40, 45, 50. Day 6 is 30. Day 7 is 35. Day 8 is 40. Day 9 is 45. And day 10 is 50.

How much money will be in the nickel jar on Day 14?

70¢

Show how you figured this out.

(50), 55, 60, 65, 70¢
Day 10 Day 11 Day 12 Day 13 Day 14

Roshaun's Work

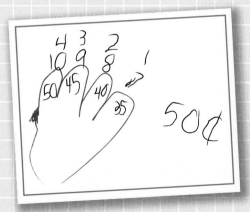

Paige's Work

Some students start from the beginning, without using the information they already have in the table, and count ten 5s. These students do understand the relationship between the number of days and the amount of money in the jar but are not able to build on the information they already have in the table. However, they do meet the benchmarks for this unit.

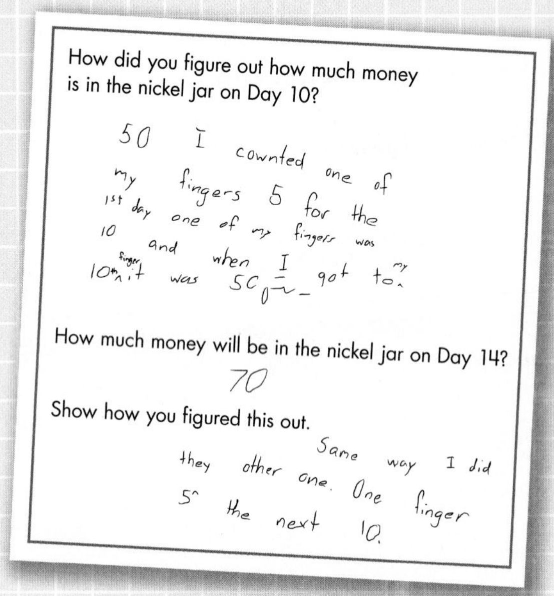

A few second graders use the information already in the table to calculate the amount of money for Day 10 and Day 14. For example, one student combined the amount for Day 4 and the amount for Day 6 to determine the amount for Day 10 and then added on another 20¢ (representing the amount of Day 4) to get the amount for Day 14.

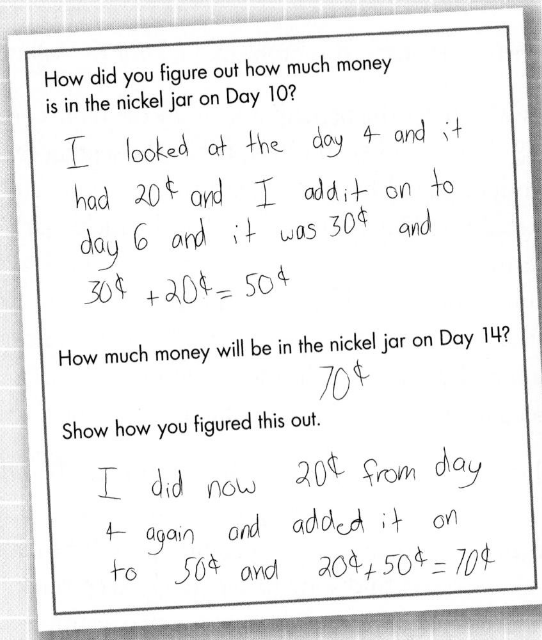

How did you figure out how much money is in the nickel jar on Day 10?

50   I cownted one of my fingers 5 for the 1st day one of my fingers was 10 and when I got to. 10th it was 50 ﹣

How much money will be in the nickel jar on Day 14?

70

Show how you figured this out.

Same way I did they other one. One finger 5^ the next 10.

Amaya's Work

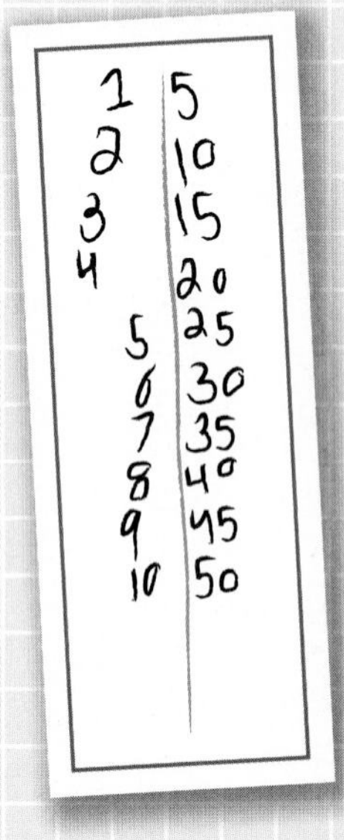

How did you figure out how much money is in the nickel jar on Day 10?

I looked at the day 4 and it had 20¢ and I addit on to day 6 and it was 30¢ and 30¢ + 20¢ = 50¢

How much money will be in the nickel jar on Day 14?

70¢

Show how you figured this out.

I did now 20¢ from day 4 again and added it on to 50¢ and 20¢ + 50¢ = 70¢

Jacy's Work

1	5
2	10
3	15
4	20
5	25
6	30
7	35
8	40
9	45
10	50

Gregory's Work

This student doubled the amount in the jar on Day 5 to get the amount for Day 10, and then added on four more 5s to get the amount for Day 14.

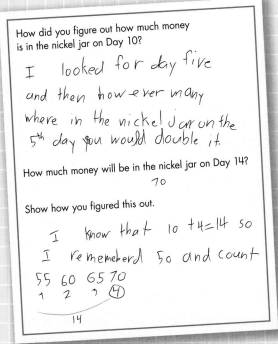

How did you figure out how much money is in the nickel jar on Day 10?

I looked for day five and then how-ever many where in the nickel jar on the 5th day you would double it.

How much money will be in the nickel jar on Day 14?

70

Show how you figured this out.

I know that 10 +4=14 so I rememeberd 50 and count 55 60 65 70

14

Jeffrey's Work

A few students do understand the meaning of the values in the table but make a counting mistake in figuring out the amount of money in the jar on Day 10 and/or Day 14. However, for this assessment, what is most important is that students demonstrate an understanding of the relationship between the number of days and the amount of money in the jar. Students who have a correct strategy but make a minor calculation or counting error are still considered to have met the benchmark for this unit. For example, Lonzell correctly counted on four more 5s, but started at 25 instead of 35. However, this student's reasoning for finding the amount of money in the jar on Day 14 gives further evidence that he understands how the number of days and the amount of money in the jar are related.

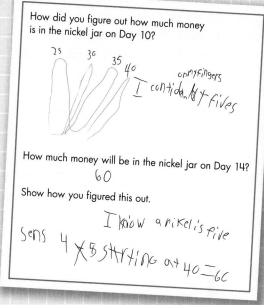

How did you figure out how much money is in the nickel jar on Day 10?

25 30 35 40 on my fingers

I contid..ly..y fives

How much money will be in the nickel jar on Day 14?

60

Show how you figured this out.

I know a nikel is five

sens 4 X 5 starting at 40 = 60

Lonzell's Work

Partially Meeting the Benchmarks

Some students fill in the amounts for Days 5 and 6 correctly and fill in the two sentences correctly, but do not correctly determine the amount of money in the jar on Day 10 and/or Day 14. These students are able to follow the pattern in a table, as long as the values are in order with no gaps. They probably determine the values for Days 5 and 6 by extending the sequence of multiples of five that they see in the second column. They can read the values from a row of the table. However, they are not yet sure how the two numbers in the row of a table are connected to one another and to the situation the table represents.

Students who are not yet sure about how the two quantities are related make two common mistakes. For Day 10, some students calculate 35¢. These students simply look down the second column and add on another 5¢, as if there were no gap in the table. They have the idea that 5¢ is added each day, but they do not recognize what the 10 in the first column means. They calculate for Day 10 as if it were Day 7. For example, one student wrote, "I counted by 5s seven times. 5, 10, 15, 20, 25, 30, 35."

Other students write 60¢ for Day 10. These students are doubling the amount for Day 6, remembering that in some tables with which they worked in this unit, they were able to use doubling. Again, these students are not always connecting the two quantities in the row of a table with the situation they represent. They are manipulating numbers in a way that worked in some cases, but are not making meaning of the particular values in this table:

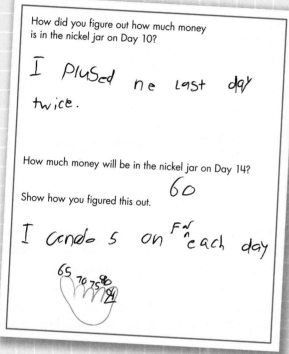

How did you figure out how much money is in the nickel jar on Day 10?

I PluSed ne last day twice.

How much money will be in the nickel jar on Day 14?

60

Show how you figured this out.

I cando 5 on F each day

65 70 75 80

Monisha's Work

It is important to look at these students' responses to the question about Day 14 for additional evidence about their understanding of the relationship between the two quantities. Some students answer this question correctly, even though they did not answer the question about Day 10 correctly. Although they do not yet fully understand how rows in the table represent two related quantities, they do understand that 5¢ is put in the jar each day, as does Monisha above. Another example is Esteban, who wrote 35¢ for Day 10 but calculated 70¢ correctly for Day 14 by counting by five 14 times.

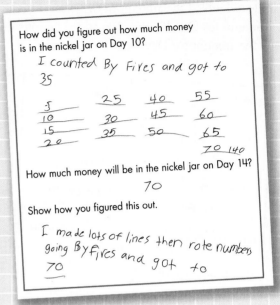

How did you figure out how much money is in the nickel jar on Day 10?

I counted By Fives and got to 35

5	25	40	55
10	30	45	60
15	35	50	65
20	35	50	70 140

How much money will be in the nickel jar on Day 14?

70

Show how you figured this out.

I made lots of lines then rote numbers going By Fives and got to 70

Esteban's Work

Not Meeting the Benchmarks

Students who cannot fill in rows 5 and 6 or the two sentences correctly do not understand how the table represents the nickel jar situation. This may be because they have not yet made sense of what the numbers in a table mean and how they show a relationship between two changing quantities. In this case, you probably already know from their work throughout the unit that these students are not making sense of tables as representations. Another possibility is that some students did not understand and visualize this new ratio situation. In this case, you might want to talk through the situation with these students, using an actual container or pictures of what the jar looks like on each successive day, and then ask them to try filling in the table again.

Problem 2: Shape Patterns

In End-of-Unit Assessment: Shape Patterns (M16–17) students determine what the 11th shape and the 16th shape will be if an AB pattern is extended.

Then, they determine what the 12th and 16th shapes will be if an AAB pattern is extended.

Benchmark addressed

Benchmark 3: Extend a repeating pattern and determine what element of the pattern will be in a particular position (e.g., the 16th position) if the pattern keeps going.

In order to meet the benchmark, students' work should show that they can:

- Determine what shape in an AB repeating shape pattern will be in a particular position;

- Explain how they figured this out.

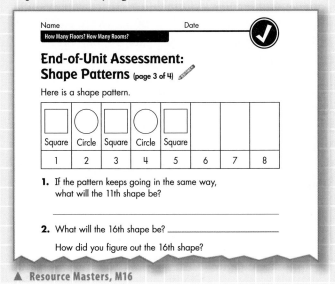

▲ **Resource Masters, M16**

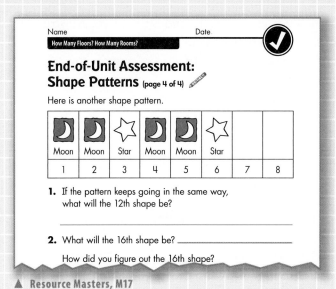

▲ **Resource Masters, M17**

Meeting the Benchmark

Students who meet the benchmark can continue at least the AB shape pattern, determine what shapes will be in the 11th (square) and 16th (circle) positions in the pattern, and explain their thinking. Some students continue the pattern shape by shape and count to the positions they need. For example, Juanita explained that she used her fingers to count from 8 up to 11 and then to 16, and then named the shapes on her fingers.

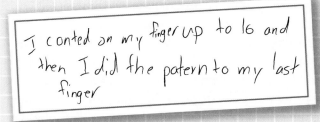

Juanita's Work

These students are not yet using the structure of the repeating pattern to help them determine how the pattern continues. Rather, they are adding on to the pattern one element at a time.

Some students, like Nadia and Luis, use the AB structure of the pattern to help them solve the problem. They recognize the sequence of even, or "counting by 2s" numbers.

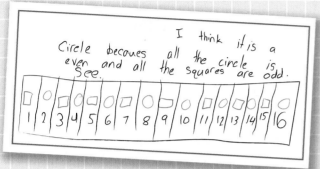

Nadia's Work

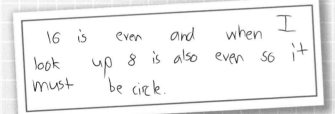

Luis's Work

The AAB repeating pattern (moon-moon-star) is more difficult because it has a three-element structure and because the part of the pattern given on the sheet (eight shapes) does not end with a complete unit of the pattern. The eighth element is a moon, the second element of the moon-moon-star unit. Many second graders do not solve this more difficult pattern correctly. Students who continue the pattern shape by shape, as they did with the AB pattern, may be successful in identifying the correct shapes for the 12th and 16th positions, if they carefully keep track. Yama's work shows this case.

Yama's Work

A few second graders can use the structure of the repeating pattern to help them find the correct shapes for the 12th and 16th positions. For example, one student wrote, "Numbers that are made up of 3s are stars."

Students who are able to extend this pattern and determine the shapes for the 12th and 16th positions are doing very well in understanding repeating patterns, beyond what is expected for most second graders.

However, many students are not able to keep track of this pattern easily, or lapse into alternating a moon with a star, rather than following the moon-moon-star pattern. Some students incorrectly assume that the shape in the 16th position will be the same as the shape in the 8th position, as it would be for an AB pattern.

Partially Meeting the Benchmark

Some students may be able to extend both patterns correctly but may make a counting error or make one mistake in the pattern sequence.

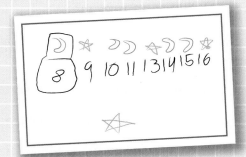

Alberto's Work

For example, Alberto skips 12 in his counting sequence, although he continues the pattern correctly. For students who make minor errors like this one, talking through their work with them will give you more information about what they understand. Some students may see their own error almost immediately once they start explaining their work. This indicates that they do, in fact, understand the structure of the pattern, what the unit of the pattern is, and how to extend the pattern. In this case, these students have met the benchmark for this problem.

Other students correctly extend the AB pattern but are not able to extend the AAB pattern. These students may not have a grasp of how a pattern with more than two elements is structured as a series of repeating units. For example, Jeffrey completed the pattern on the worksheet through shape 8, and then continued counting from 9 to 16 on the same row of eight shapes.

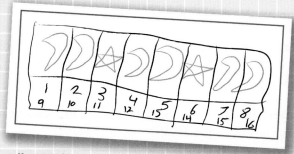

Jeffrey's Work

This student may be generalizing from what has worked in the past with an AB pattern, but this method does not work here because the pattern has a unit of three elements (AAB). The student may not see what the unit of this pattern is and does not realize that the AA (moon-moon) part of the pattern in positions 7 and 8 should be followed by the B part of the pattern (star) in position 9. To get more information about this student's response, you can ask, "Do you see a part of the pattern that repeats over and over again? Can you do a body movement pattern that is like this one?"

Not Meeting the Benchmark

Students who cannot continue the AB pattern in some way to determine what the 11th and 16th shapes are can benefit from more work extending patterns with cubes and pattern blocks. These students may not have had prior experience of the kind provided in the Grade 1 unit *Color, Shape, and Number Patterns*. The activities *Make a Train* and *Break a Train* from that unit would be beneficial to give these students additional work in making patterns and seeing how a repeating pattern is made up of repetitions of a unit.

Dialogue Box

"It's the Same Thing as Up There on the Table"

The class is focusing on the "Building A" chart.

Number of Floors	Number of Rooms
1	3
2	6
3	9
4	12
5	15
6	18

Teacher: What is happening in this column? [The teacher points to the first column, the number of floors.]

Jeffrey: It's going by one. The number, it goes by 1s.

Teacher: How about the column for the total number of rooms?

Jacy: It's going by 3s.

Esteban: Every time, when you have the 3, it's counting three more on for the next number there.

Nate: You're counting by 3s, because if you count 3 plus 3 is 6, and you do the same thing for the 6 and it goes to 9, and the same thing to the 9 and it goes to 12.

So far, the students are describing the pattern they see in the table as they look at the numbers, but it is not clear whether they are connecting these numbers to what they represent in the cube buildings. The teacher focuses students' attention on one row of the table to help them think through that connection. She points to the second row of the table.

Teacher: So, what does this mean going across? What does the two mean and what does the six mean?

Rochelle: I think there will be two floors and six rooms.

Teacher: What does that mean, two floors and six rooms? What does she mean by that?

Tia: It means you go up two floors and you have six rooms.

Simon: It means if you put three on top, you have six.

Teacher: Three on top of what? Who can show me with the cubes what this second row means?

Lonzell holds up a cube building with two floors, three cubes per floor.

Lonzell: There are two floors, and you have three cubes on this one, and if you add three on for the second floor, that would make six.

Rochelle: I think it's because there's three cubes on every floor.

Teacher: So who can finish this sentence about this row, "If I have two floors in my building, I'll have . . ."?

Amaya: Six rooms.

Carla: If you have two floors, then you're going to have six rooms.

Teacher: And what if I add another floor? How many rooms will I have then?

Rochelle: Nine. I counted 3, 6, 9.

Yama: Three floors and nine rooms. It means [pointing to the model of the building] you count up all of them and there are nine.

Teacher: Did anyone look at the table to think about my question about three floors?

Henry: Isn't it the same thing? I need some help. [Henry reaches for the cube building.] It's the same thing! It doesn't matter what you're counting, you can just add the three. You add the two 3s, and then another three, and it's the same thing as up there on the table. It's nine.

In this dialogue, the teacher is helping students think about how the numbers in the table represent the relationship between total number of floors and total number of rooms in the cube building. When students focus on the number patterns in a column, they sometimes see the number pattern (e.g., counting by 3s) but lose their sense of how those numbers tell a story about how the building is changing as more floors are added. By focusing their attention on individual rows, students are thinking about the relationship between the two numbers and between the total number of floors and total number of rooms. In Investigation 1, students need to continually move back and forth between the table and the situation it represents. Notice how Henry, who seems to have a good idea of how the table represents the building, needs to look at the building again to articulate for himself and others that what is in the third row of the table represents the same counting by 3s that he sees in the building.

Why Is It Counting by 3s?

Number of Trapezoids	Number of Triangles
1	3
2	6
3	9
4	12
5	15

Teacher: What kinds of things can you see on this table?

Holly: If you have one trapezoid you are going to have 2, 3, 4, 5 [drags her finger down the first column].

Teacher: OK, so you are looking at this column here [points to first column]. What kind of information can you tell me about this row here [points to second row]?

Anita: If you have two trapezoids, you need six triangles.

Roshaun: You're counting by 3s. 'Cause there are two trapezoids and three on each one.

Teacher: And what did you say again about this column [points to second column]?

Roshaun: It's counting by 3s.

Teacher: What does that mean? Why is it counting by 3s?

Carolina: You had one trapezoid and you said you want the triangles to equal one trapezoid, and it takes three to match this [points to a trapezoid].

The teacher puts out an arrangement of two trapezoids covered with six triangles.

Teacher: Why do you count by 3s? Why not 2s or 5s?

Leigh: You put the trapezoid on the floor and you add the three triangles, and it's different than counting by 2s because you add one more. It wouldn't be counting by 2s because you need one more triangle to fill up the trapezoid.

Teacher: What would the next picture be on the rug if I put down another trapezoid? How many total triangles would there be? How many altogether?

Various students: Nine.

Teacher: Why can't it be eight?

Alberto: Because it's counting by 3s.

Teacher: Why are we counting by 3s?

Jacy: 'Cause this [points to a trapezoid] got more space for three.

Leo: 'Cause you're making the triangles equal the trapezoids.

In this conversation, the teacher repeatedly asks students to explain why they are counting by 3s. By asking a question like "Why not 2s or 5s?" she is indicating that 3, 6, 9 is not just a number pattern, but is connected to some kind of "threeness" in the situation the numbers are representing. In response to her questions, students explain in different ways that they are counting by 3s because there are three triangles for every trapezoid.

Comparing Tables

This class is comparing all of the tables about cube buildings and pattern blocks in the final discussion in Session 1.6. The teacher points to the "Rhombus and Triangle" table and the "Hexagon and Trapezoid" table.

Teacher: Why are the numbers in these two tables the same? We used different blocks. This one is about covering hexagons with trapezoids, but this one is about covering rhombuses with triangles. Who can explain it? Who has an idea?

Jeffrey: There's no difference between this one [points to "Rhombus and Triangle" table] and this one [points to "Hexagon and Trapezoid" table].

Teacher: OK, Jeffrey, can you explain that?

Jeffrey: You have to put two of these [holds up a triangle] there [picks up a rhombus] and you just have to put two of these [a trapezoid] there [puts it on top of hexagon].

Teacher: So what are you thinking about the hexagon and the trapezoid?

Jeffrey: That there is going to be one hexagon and two trapezoids just like that one [points to the "Rhombus and Triangle" table].

Teacher: Does anyone see any other charts that have numbers that are the same as each other?

Monisha: Building A. Two floors have six rooms because three plus three equals six. And three floors have nine rooms. It's the same as the one with the triangles [pointing to the "Trapezoid and Triangle" table].

Teacher: Who else wants to say something about the "Building A" chart and the "Trapezoid and Triangle" table?

Gregory: Three would go into nine 'cause we're counting by 3s. It takes three triangles to fill up one trapezoid. It has the same numbers right here and right here.

Leo: On one trapezoid there's three triangles and on one floor there's three rooms.

Teacher: Is there any other time we have this relationship of one to three?

Juanita: One hexagon and three rhombuses.

Teacher: And how is that the same? Carolina, you wanted to say something about that one.

Carolina: It's like a floor with three rooms. [She stacks three cubes on top of the hexagon.]

Second graders are beginning to develop the idea that there is something similar about situations that have the same underlying constant ratio. For example, Leo says, "On one trapezoid there's three triangles and on one floor there's three rooms." He seems to be noticing the one-to-three relationship in both of these contexts. Many students may not be able to explain their ideas adequately in words. Pay close attention to students' gestures, and ask them to demonstrate their ideas with materials, as Carolina does. By putting three cubes on top of the hexagon, she seems to be expressing something like, "three cubes on one floor of a building is like three triangles covering a hexagon."

"The Reds Are Uneven"

Students in this class have completed work on the red-blue pattern on *Student Activity Book* page 38. As they gather for a discussion of this pattern, the teacher has put a large number strip on a piece of chart paper with the first six boxes colored in the red-blue pattern.

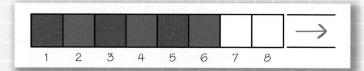

Teacher: Before we fill in the next few boxes, who can tell me what color would be in square 9?

Chen: It's red!

Tia: The reds are uneven. Because it's on 1 and 3.

Melissa: They're odd.

Henry: And the blues are on evens.

Teacher: So, what do you mean by *even?*

Leigh: When you have a number and you keep on adding 2s.

Anita: It's skipping like 2, 4, 6, 8, 10, 12, 14, 16, 18, 20, and it's skipping red, blue, red, blue, red, blue.

Leo: I think even means they both equal the same thing.

Paige: [pointing at the 2 on the number strip] *Even* means that this one is even and then this one is even [pointing to the 4] because it's two more, and it goes 2, 2, 2 [pointing at 6, 8, 10].

Teacher: All right, so it has something to do with 2s. Let's see what you think about this. If I have 11 students who go to the park, do I have an even or an odd number of students?

Many students: Odd.

Teacher: Why is it odd?

Rochelle: An odd number is a number that doesn't have two numbers inside—like, six has three and three.

Jacy: Ten has five and five.

Juan: An odd number is one that you can't share with your friends. Like, if I have one ice cream cone, I can't share it with my friend.

Alberto: I never knew this, but my mom told me. You skip a number, in between, and you go to the next number.

Nadia: But what if it's one and a half and one and a half?

When the students bring up the terms *odd* and *even*, the teacher pauses to see what they understand about these two kinds of numbers. These second graders offer several good ideas about odd and even numbers. Anita, Leigh, and Paige are thinking of an even number as a number that is composed of 2s. Leo, Rochelle, and Juan are thinking of an even number as a number that can be split into two equal parts and an odd number as one that cannot be split in two equal parts. These are two important ways of defining even and odd numbers.

Nadia is wondering why 3 is an odd number because it can be split it into one and a half and one and a half. She is raising a good question about the second definition of *even* posed by the students—a number that can be split into two equal parts. The teacher could acknowledge this as a very good question and might tell the students at this point that the official definition of *even* is that the two equal parts have to be whole numbers, with no halves. Some students might bring up the point that if you could use halves, every number would be even.

Alberto makes an interesting statement about skipping numbers. He is probably referring to odd numbers since the conversation at that point is focused on odd numbers. An important question to raise would be whether this idea applies to even numbers or to odd numbers. Second graders are often interested in the fact that both odd and even numbers "skip one number in between" and both odd and even numbers are sequences that involve counting by 2s or adding 2s. One sequence starts with 1 and goes up by 2, while the other sequence starts at 2 (or at 0) and goes up by 2.

Dialogue Box

Counting by 3s

Students in this class have completed work on the yellow-red-blue pattern on *Student Activity Book* pages 40–41. The teacher has a picture of the beginning of the number strip for this pattern and asks the students for their list of numbers that go with blue. They list the numbers on the board.

3, 6, 9, 12, 15, 18, 21, 24, 27, 30

Teacher: I'd like you to study the numbers and think about them. What do you notice about this list of numbers? Turn and tell someone what you think.

After giving students a short time to talk in pairs, the teacher asks for students' ideas.

Luis: They are counting by 3s.

Carolina: It's going by 3s.

Esteban: It's skipping two colors and it's skipping two cubes.

Teacher: What do you mean it's skipping two cubes?

Esteban: 1, 2, blue, 1, 2, blue, 1, 2, blue.

Amaya: I want to say that this makes sense when I said 3, 6, 9, 12, but this is the part that doesn't make sense—when it goes 18, 21, 24, 27, 30.

Teacher: Are you saying that it gets kind of confusing with those higher numbers? That they are not as familiar as when you count 3, 6, 9, 12?

Amaya: Yeah.

Teacher: So when you got to 12 and you needed to figure out where the next blue was, how did you find the next number?

Jacy: Me and Rochelle looked at the number line and we counted three more.

Teacher: So where did you start and how did you count?

Jacy: We started on 12 and we went 13, 14, 15.

Teacher: Some of you were saying that this list is counting by 3s. Why is it counting by 3s?

Gregory: Because three plus three is six, then plus three is nine. You keep plussing on 3s.

Teacher: Okay. It's adding three each time. But why is it adding 3s for the blue? Why isn't it counting by 2s?

Juanita: I think it's three because the blue is at the end. So you have to count the first one, and that would be a yellow, and the second one is a red. Then we get to blue if we count one more.

Teacher: We have to keep counting by 3s to get to blue.

Leigh: It's like when we're hopping something. You have to hop twice to get to the third.

Teacher: So, you said it was the end one, Juanita, like it's the last one [holds up the yellow-red-blue unit of the pattern]. I'm looking at these three cubes, and the blue is the end one.

As students consider the number sequence associated with the blue cubes in the yellow-red-blue cube train, they are thinking through what it means to "count by" a number. Juanita describes how the yellow-red-blue cube train is a group of three. Since the repeating pattern is made up of these units of three and "the blue is at the end," the number of each blue cube is three more than the number of the previous blue cube. Other students—like Esteban and Leigh—think of a group of three in two parts: the parts you "skip" and the part you land on. When you count by 3s, you "skip" two and land on the next one. Leigh and Esteban have also identified this last cube as important just as Juanita did. As students talk, they are visualizing a series of equal groups of cubes and how counting by the number of cubes in each group gives them the total number of cubes. This work lays the foundation for the operation of multiplication. The teacher's questions—"Why is it counting by 3s? Why isn't it counting by 2s?"—help focus students' attention on the connection between the number sequence and the cube train that is built from groups of three.

Student Math Handbook

The *Student Math Handbook* pages related to this unit are pictured on the following pages. This book is designed to be used flexibly: as a resource for students doing classwork, as a book students can take home for reference while doing homework and playing math games with their families, and as a reference for families to better understand the work their children are doing in class.

When students take the *Student Math Handbook* home, they and their families can discuss these pages together to reinforce or enhance students' understanding of the mathematical concepts and games in this unit.

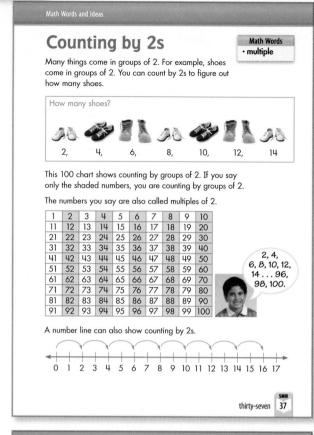

Counting by 2s

Math Words
· multiple

Many things come in groups of 2. For example, shoes come in groups of 2. You can count by 2s to figure out how many shoes.

How many shoes?

2, 4, 6, 8, 10, 12, 14

This 100 chart shows counting by groups of 2. If you say only the shaded numbers, you are counting by groups of 2.

The numbers you say are also called multiples of 2.

1	2	3	4	5	6	7	8	9	10
11	12	13	14	15	16	17	18	19	20
21	22	23	24	25	26	27	28	29	30
31	32	33	34	35	36	37	38	39	40
41	42	43	44	45	46	47	48	49	50
51	52	53	54	55	56	57	58	59	60
61	62	63	64	65	66	67	68	69	70
71	72	73	74	75	76	77	78	79	80
81	82	83	84	85	86	87	88	89	90
91	92	93	94	95	96	97	98	99	100

2, 4, 6, 8, 10, 12, 14 . . . 96, 98, 100.

A number line can also show counting by 2s.

0 1 2 3 4 5 6 7 8 9 10 11 12 13 14 15 16 17

thirty-seven **SMH 37**

▲ Math Words and Ideas, p. 37

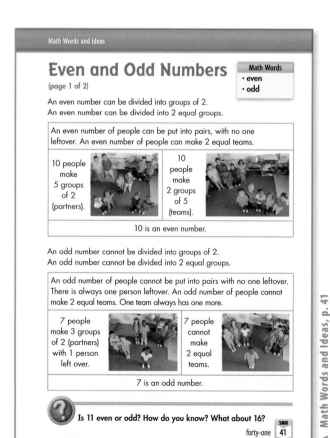

Even and Odd Numbers
(page 1 of 2)

Math Words
· even
· odd

An even number can be divided into groups of 2.
An even number can be divided into 2 equal groups.

An even number of people can be put into pairs, with no one leftover. An even number of people can make 2 equal teams.

10 people make 5 groups of 2 (partners).

10 people make 2 groups of 5 (teams).

10 is an even number.

An odd number cannot be divided into groups of 2.
An odd number cannot be divided into 2 equal groups.

An odd number of people cannot be put into pairs with no one leftover. There is always one person leftover. An odd number of people cannot make 2 equal teams. One team always has one more.

7 people make 3 groups of 2 (partners) with 1 person left over.

7 people cannot make 2 equal teams.

7 is an odd number.

? Is 11 even or odd? How do you know? What about 16?

forty-one **SMH 41**

▲ Math Words and Ideas, p. 41

Even and Odd Numbers
(page 2 of 2)

If you start at 0 and count by 2s, you say the even numbers.
If you start at 1 and count by 2s, you say the odd numbers.
On this 100 chart, the odd numbers are yellow.
The even numbers are green.

Odd and even numbers alternate in a pattern.

1	2	3	4	5	6	7	8	9	10
11	12	13	14	15	16	17	18	19	20
21	22	23	24	25	26	27	28	29	30
31	32	33	34	35	36	37	38	39	40
41	42	43	44	45	46	47	48	49	50
51	52	53	54	55	56	57	58	59	60
61	62	63	64	65	66	67	68	69	70
71	72	73	74	75	76	77	78	79	80
81	82	83	84	85	86	87	88	89	90
91	92	93	94	95	96	97	98	99	100

? Is 35 even or odd? How do you know? What about 60? 101?

SMH 42 forty-two

▲ Math Words and Ideas, p. 42

A Growing Pattern

Look at this example about a group of people and the number of eyes.

Math Words
• pattern

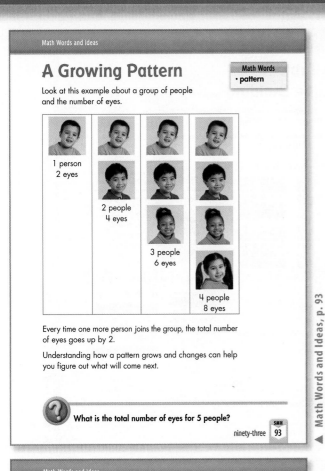

Every time one more person joins the group, the total number of eyes goes up by 2.

Understanding how a pattern grows and changes can help you figure out what will come next.

? What is the total number of eyes for 5 people?

ninety-three **SMH 93**

Math Words and Ideas, p. 93

Tables (page 1 of 2)

A table is a way to organize information.

A table is made up of columns going up and down and rows going across. Look at this table about people and eyes.

Math Words
• table
• column

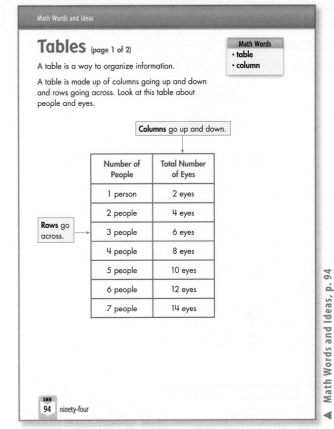

SMH 94 ninety-four

Math Words and Ideas, p. 94

Tables (page 2 of 2)

Here is the same table with only numbers. See if you can figure out what each row and column is showing.

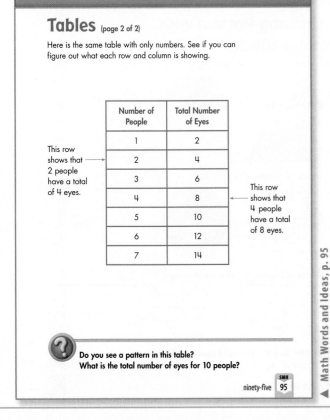

? Do you see a pattern in this table?
What is the total number of eyes for 10 people?

ninety-five **SMH 95**

Math Words and Ideas, p. 95

Another Growing Pattern

This building is being built. Each floor of this building has 5 rooms.

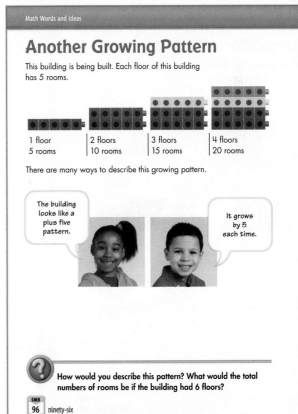

There are many ways to describe this growing pattern.

? How would you describe this pattern? What would the total numbers of rooms be if the building had 6 floors?

SMH 96 ninety-six

Math Words and Ideas, p. 96

Math Words and Ideas

A Table for a Cube Building (page 1 of 2)

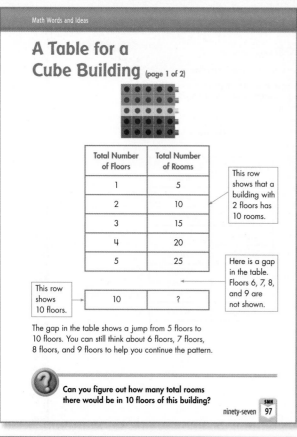

Total Number of Floors	Total Number of Rooms
1	5
2	10
3	15
4	20
5	25

This row shows that a building with 2 floors has 10 rooms.

Here is a gap in the table. Floors 6, 7, 8, and 9 are not shown.

10	?

This row shows 10 floors.

The gap in the table shows a jump from 5 floors to 10 floors. You can still think about 6 floors, 7 floors, 8 floors, and 9 floors to help you continue the pattern.

Can you figure out how many total rooms there would be in 10 floors of this building?

ninety-seven **97**

◄ Math Words and Ideas, p. 97

Math Words and Ideas

A Table for a Cube Building (page 2 of 2)

Can you figure out how many total rooms there would be on 10 floors of this building?

Several students thought about this problem and figured it out in different ways.

Leo counted by 5s ten times.

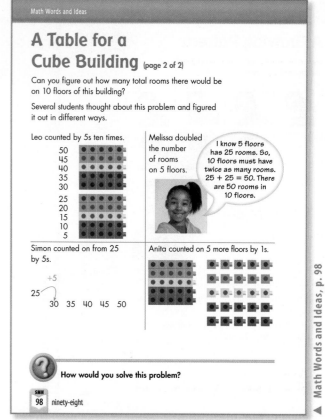

50
45
40
35
30
25
20
15
10
5

Melissa doubled the number of rooms on 5 floors.

I know 5 floors has 25 rooms. So, 10 floors must have twice as many rooms. 25 + 25 = 50. There are 50 rooms in 10 floors.

Simon counted on from 25 by 5s.

$$+5$$
25
30 35 40 45 50

Anita counted on 5 more floors by 1s.

How would you solve this problem?

98 ninety-eight

◄ Math Words and Ideas, p. 98

Math Words and Ideas

Pattern Block Shapes

Here are the pattern block shapes.

hexagon

triangle

trapezoid

rhombus

square

rhombus

ninety-nine **99**

◄ Math Words and Ideas, p. 99

Math Words and Ideas

A Growing Pattern with Pattern Blocks

One trapezoid can be covered by 3 triangles.

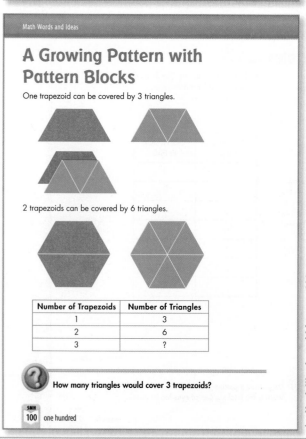

2 trapezoids can be covered by 6 triangles.

Number of Trapezoids	Number of Triangles
1	3
2	6
3	?

How many triangles would cover 3 trapezoids?

100 one hundred

◄ Math Words and Ideas, p. 100

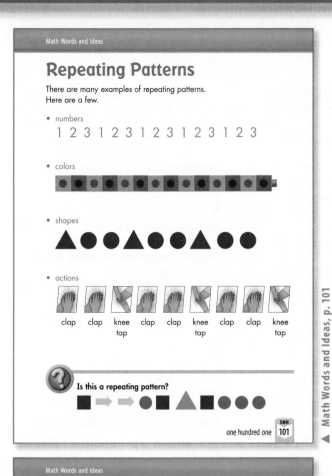

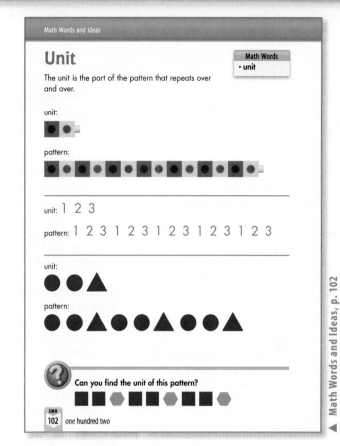

Repeating Patterns
on a Number Strip

A number strip can help record a repeating pattern.

1	2	3	4	5	6	7	8	9	10

In this repeating pattern, each square is numbered.

The 1st square is green.
The 2nd square is blue.
The 3rd square is green.
The 4th square is blue.
The 5th square is green.
The 6th square is blue.
The 7th square is green.
The 8th square is blue.
The 9th square is green.
The 10th square is blue.

When a pattern repeats, you can use what you know to predict what will come next.

If this pattern keeps repeating in the same way, what color will go in the 12th square? Will the 15th square be blue or green? If the pattern repeats for 20 squares, how many squares will be blue?

one hundred three   **SMH 103**

▲ **Math Words and Ideas, p. 103**

Index